57235

# DATA
## COMMUNICATIONS
## IN BUSINESS

*An Introduction*

*Edited by*

**Edgar C. Gentle, Jr.**

*Data Communications Planning Administrator*
*American Telephone and Telegraph Company*

**American Telephone and Telegraph Company**
**New York**

*Copies of this book may be ordered from:*

PUBLISHERS SERVICE COMPANY—Room 600
75 Varick Street
New York, N. Y.  10013

Paperback Edition ............$2.00
Hard Cover Edition ........ 4.00

The above prices include handling and postage

ii

Prepared by the American Telephone and Telegraph Company
with the advice and guidance of the following Educational Advisory Panel:

**Dr. E. Dana Gibson, Professor**
*School of Business Administration*
*San Diego State College*

**Dr. Harry Huffman, Professor**
*School of Education*
*The Ohio State University*

**Dr. Norman F. Kallaus, Associate Professor**
*College of Business Administration*
*University of Iowa*

# ACKNOWLEDGMENT

The thoughtful reader of this book will quickly realize that its subject matter touches upon many aspects of the rapidly evolving relationship of man to machine and machine to machine. Because of the many areas that had to be considered in preparing this introductory text, the advice and active participation of many persons were required.

In particular, we wish to acknowledge the work of Lauren R. Asplund, Andrew L. Cobb, and the other members of the Data Communications Planning Section of the American Telephone and Telegraph Company.

We are also deeply grateful to Dr. E. Dana Gibson, Dr. Harry Huffman and Dr. Norman F. Kallaus, members of our Educational Advisory Panel, to whom must go much of the credit for whatever success we have achieved in designing this book for the needs of the educational community.

To these men and to all others who contributed their time and effort in the preparation of this volume, we express our sincere appreciation.

**Edgar C. Gentle, Jr.**
*Data Communications Planning Administrator*
*American Telephone and Telegraph Company*
*November 1, 1965.*

# FOREWORD

The fabric of our society is woven together by the contributions of individuals and by their abilities to communicate their thoughts and actions. The aggregate dimensions of such communications are increasingly dependent upon efficient systems of transmitting data by electrical means. This book presents the fundamental ideas involved in developing effective uses of data communications. More importantly, it provides an insight into the way that administrators of business, industry, education and government benefit from integrated information systems which merge data processing and communication techniques.

Recent developments in both the concepts associated with business information systems and the hardware associated with computers have had a significant impact on management education and practice. Now we see further changes as new concepts and new technological developments are applied to the movement of business data over longer distances. These changes influence the pattern of management decisions and the very structure of organizations. Questions of centralization, decentralization, and related authorities and responsibilities are examples of management patterns that are being deeply influenced by changes in the field of data communications.

This book was written by staff members of the Bell System. Our role as consultants was to advise and guide the staff group. In particular, we were asked to represent the interests of faculty members at the collegiate level who might be seeking course materials in this new field.

The insight that can be gained by a study of the materials in this book will not make a data communications expert of the reader. It will, however, provide students of business administration, present and future managers, and present and future business teachers with a good introduction to the subject. The future manager can gain a better understanding of how data processing and data communications can be merged for management decision making. Teachers in the field will be able to supplement discussions of information systems and "automation" with authoritative information on data communications.

E. Dana Gibson
Harry Huffman
Norman F. Kallaus

vii

# TABLE OF CONTENTS

Foreword ............... vii

List of Figures ............. x

### CHAPTER I

**The Meaning of Data Communications** .......... 1

Definition — The Forms and Uses of Data Communications — Data Communications and Business Information Systems — Data Communications and Data Processing — The Function of Data Communications — Summary

### CHAPTER II

**The Role of Data Communications** ...... 8

The Information Explosion — Data Communications as an Aid to Government — Data Communications and the Firm — Data Communications and the Manager — Summary

### CHAPTER III

**Data Communications in Management** ............. 24

Departmental Applications of Data Communications — Business Information Systems — The Westinghouse Information System — Summary

### CHAPTER IV

**Communications Problems in Information Systems** ...... 39

Belated Information — Outdated Information — Inaccessible Information — Expensive Information — Inaccurate Information — Mutilated Information — Summary

### CHAPTER V

**Planning a Data Communications System** ... 49

Identify and Define Problem — Gather and Analyze the Facts — Design Alternative Data Communications Systems — Determine the Costs of Each Alternative System — Evaluate the Alternative Systems — Implement the Selected System — Follow Up — Summary

### CHAPTER VI

**Trends in Data Communications** .......... 81

Computers and Data Communications — On-Line Real-Time System — Semi-Real Time — Voice Communication in Computer Systems — Terminal Equipment — Simplification of Operation — Wider Variety of Terminal Equipment — Communications Technology — Conclusion

**Case Studies** ............ 96

I King Construction Company
II Custer Oil Company
III Franklin Department Stores

**Supplementary Information** ............. 116

Data Transmission Terminal Equipment
Communication Services
Communication Switching
Glossary of Data Communications Terms
Data Communications Bibliography

**Index** ................. 161

# LIST OF FIGURES

1. Data processing equipment reaching beyond its own room .............. 5
2. Communication channels provide access to information stored in computers ............. 10
3. Merged companies establish a centralized data processing center .. 15
4. Different company locations have access to a data processing capability ............... 19
5. Construction company information system .... 21
6. Teleprinter system for an automobile assembly line ................. 27
7. Information flow in a Business Information System ................ 30
8. Conceptual view of the composition of an information system .... 31
9. The Westinghouse Teleprinter Message Switching System .. 34
10. The Westinghouse Automated Order Processing and Inventory Control System ...... 35
11. A communication system to handle payroll information for a wood products company .. 41
12. An automated telephone company supplies ordering system .. 42, 43
13. Chart showing the information flow in a typical company .............. 52
14. Geographic diagram of the information flow in a typical company .... 53
15. Basic distribution patterns ......................... 55
16. A communication network for a typical two-division company ......... 57
17. A typical sales order form 60

18. A sales order form designed for use with teleprinters ................. 62
19. Chart showing the calculation of busy hour traffic flowing in one direction between two points ............... 64
20. A communication system for transmitting punched paper tape and receiving in punched card form ....................... 69
21. Block diagram of a data communication system ..................................... 72
22. Summary of steps involved in planning a data communication system ..................................... 79
23. General Eleetric Data Communications Processor: DATANET-30 ....... 82
24. Data collection system .. 84
25. A sample telephone company service order prepared in a conversation mode ................. 89
26. Keydata Corporation's time-shared computer center ................. 90
27. The experimental PICTUREPHONE telephone ................. 91
28. Distribution chart for Custer Oil Company .. 101
29. Five-part delivery ticket for Custer Oil Company ..................... 106
30. Distribution chart for Franklin Department Stores ................. 110
31. Merchandise tag for Franklin Department Stores ..................................... 113
32. Data Set ................ 118
33. Data set used as a connecting device .......... 119
34. Pushbutton card dialer telephone ................. 120
35. Keyboard printer model of a teleprinter ........ 121

36. Keyboard of a teleprinter ................................. 122

37. Automatic send and receive model of a teleprinter ................................. 123

38. The American Standard Code for Information Interchange ............ 124

39. Tally paper tape transmission terminals with compatible DATA-PHONE data sets 125

40. The IBM 1001 Data Transmission Terminal with compatible DATA-PHONE data set .. 126

41. The RCA Model 5907 Magnetic Tape Terminal ................................. 127

42. Diagram of a transmission control terminal arrangement ............ 128

43. The Victor Electrowriter transceiver ............ 130

44. Stewart-Warner Corporation's "dial/Datafax" facsimile terminal with compatible DATA-PHONE data set .. 131

45. Teleregister visual display terminal ............... 132

46. Button arrangement on a DATA-PHONE data set ............................ 134

47. Map of Wide Area Telephone Service calling areas ...................... 135

48. Typical terminal used for automatic teleprinter exchange services 136

xi

### Chapter I

# THE MEANING OF
# DATA
# COMMUNICATIONS

Among the many characteristics that have enabled man to rise above all other forms of life on earth is his ability to communicate across time and space. Many lower animals are capable of transmitting information within their immediate environment. But only man has learned to record information, and thus communicate across time, and to send information beyond his immediate environment, thereby communicating across space. The progress of civilization is closely paralleled by improvements and setbacks in man's systems of communication.

Contemporary man, faced with a surging technology and increasingly complex problems of organization, has had to develop entirely new methods of dealing with the enormous amount of information generated daily by both the private and public sectors of society. He has also had to find ways of collecting information from, and transmitting it to, widely dispersed points with ever increasing speed. Data communications is designed to fulfill this requirement of rapid transmission of information.

## Definition

Although almost any process of transmitting information may be thought of as a form of data communications, the term is usually limited to one particular area of technology. In this sense, a data communication system must have these two characteristics: (1) the data, or information, is transformed into a special code and (2) the data is moved, or transmitted, by electronic means. Data communications may thus be defined as *the movement of encoded information by means of electrical transmission systems*. The transmission system includes input/output devices, the electrical transmission links proper and, in many instances, related communication switching systems.

The terms data and information will be used interchangeably

1

in this book although there is a subtle difference between the two.[1] Data may be regarded as one or more facts, not necessarily meaningful. Information, however, is always meaningful. For example, the apparently meaningless series of digits 0486752250 could be called data. To a payroll clerk, however, to whom the figures mean that employee number 0486 worked 7.5 hours and should be paid $22.50, the series of digits would be information. Since data[2] is transmitted through a data communication system in order to reach someone to whom it is meaningful, in this text data and information will be considered synonymous.

## The Forms and Uses of Data Communications

Following are some examples of data communications at work:

1. A hotel confirms a salesman's room reservation in another city by teleprinter communication with the chain's central office.
2. A builder receives a sketch of a change in an architectural drawing over a handwriting transmission system.
3. A police officer at a remote location uses a facsimile system to dispatch a photograph to headquarters for identification purposes.
4. A branch office manager submits time-card information to the company's home office computer, using a punched card transmission system.
5. A doctor in a small town transmits an electrocardiogram of one of his patients to a distant university hospital for analysis by a heart specialist.
6. A scientist obtains a copy of a research study on space medicine from library records by means of a microfilm transmission system.
7. On Monday morning, a sales manager receives a report of the preceding week's sales via teleprinter service from the corporate data processing center.

In each of these examples, a data communication system is used to transmit information almost instantaneously over a considerable

---

[1] "Information" is a multi-faceted term in today's scientific world. The definition used in this text is drawn from the way the word is used in business. For a glimpse into the many other definitions of the word "information," see **On Human Communication,** Colin Cherry, John Wiley & Sons, Inc., New York.

[2] Although the word "data" is the plural of the noun "datum," its association with a singular verb is becoming established by common business usage.

distance. It is this capability that permits data communications to play a vital role in operations and management.

The activities of business, government and other large organizations are to a considerable extent dependent upon information and the movement of this information. The increasing compatibility of data processing and data communications is doing much to reinforce the complete systems approach now being offered in today's procedures for information handling.

## Data Communications and Business Information Systems

A Business Information System is a combination of people, data processing equipment, input/output devices and communications facilities. It supplies timely information to both management and non-management people for the planning and operation of a business. The system must accept information at the point where it is generated, transport it to the point where it is to be processed, process the information and, finally, deliver it to the point where it is to be used. If the total system were contained in one room, the role of electrical communications might be minor—perhaps just a number of wires running across the room. In practice, however, the points of collection, processing, and ultimate use are separated, and data communications assumes the key role in linking the total system.

## Data Communications and Data Processing

Data is being processed whenever office workers perform any of these types of operations:

| Operation | Example |
|---|---|
| 1. recording | typing an order or writing up stock transaction information. |
| 2. classifying | deciding how to file correspondence. |
| 3. sorting | segregating student data by class —freshmen, senior, etc. |
| 4. calculating | determining the amount to be paid to an employee for time worked. |
| 5. summarizing | writing a report. |

3

6. storing and retrieving      filing documents and taking others from the file.

In contemporary business practice, however, the term data processing implies extensive utilization of machines, in particular computers, to perform these operations.

In any discussion of the relation of data communications and data processing, it is useful to recognize that information must move within a data processing system and that this movement is a form of data communication. However, data communications extends far beyond the context of data processing, embracing as it does the movement of information to and from the point of processing. *(Figure 1.)* It permits data processing equipment to reach out and establish contact beyond the limits of its own air-conditioned room. Data communications enables a data processing facility to be used by remote locations for processing, inquiry or input of information. Operating efficiency is enhanced to the degree that basic processing equipment becomes accessible to more people for wider use in an expanded sphere of operation.

The information system of the Westinghouse Electric Corporation, a multi-product company with almost 300 locations throughout the United States and Canada, is an example of the close working relationship between data communications and data processing. Through the use of data communications, all of the company's locations are connected with the Tele-Computer Center in Pittsburgh. The Westinghouse information system is described in detail in Chapter III.

Data communications also makes it possible to design a large scale data processing system with computers in widely separated locations linked together through communication channels. Since each computer in such an arrangement has access to the data stored in the memory of other units, it is unnecessary to duplicate the contents of all the memory units. As a result, the total amount of information that can be stored in the system is increased. With this type of linkage, it is possible in a properly designed system to balance the processing load by sending any overloads of data at one location to another location that has spare processing capacity on its computer.

**The Function of
Data Communications**

It is universally recognized that communication technology is essential to all business today. A business able to function suc-

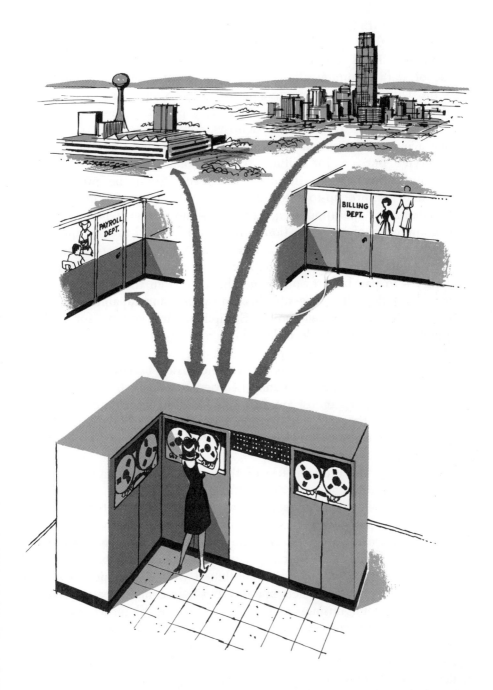

Figure 1. Data communications permits data processing equipment to reach beyond the space and time limitations of its own air-conditioned room.

cessfully without some application of communications is difficult to imagine. At a minimum, a company needs one telephone to operate. At the other extreme are companies that exist solely because of their use of communications.

Organizational size is not the only factor in determining the role of data communications. From an organization as complex as the United States Government to one as simple as a dentist's office handling its own records, there is a potential need for data communications. Doctors and dentists, for example, can transmit their account information by means of data communication facilities to service bureaus for billing. Within companies uses for data communications can be found at all levels, from the president, who may require up-to-date information on almost any aspect of the company's operation, to a production-line worker, whose report on completion of one operation must be transmitted to a computer.

It is possible that within the next decade a family may conduct many of its affairs with the help of some type of data processing facility — to pay bills, to order merchandise from the store, and to make bank deposits. Access to this data processing capability might be provided via the telephone. Equipment and systems for such applications are available today and planning is now going on for providing services of this type.

It can be seen that there is an ever-increasing *variety* of ways in which data communications may be used to benefit both business and individuals. In almost any business function — accounting, marketing, production, etc. — the combination of data processing with data communications is being employed to improve and facilitate operations of the enterprise.

Because of the growing use of these applications, many of the nation's business concerns are training their people in this field. Sears, Roebuck and Company recognizes the role of these integrated data processing arrangements in the development of an efficient information system. Training and education in systems are regularly held for management personnel with emphasis being given to the application of processing combined with communications.

The Bell System conducts one-day business communication seminars to acquaint businessmen with the uses of all forms of communications. Executives from many types of businesses from all over the country attend this one-day seminar. In addition, a two-day seminar, covering the field of communications in much greater detail for systems men and data processing managers, draws attendance from many businesses.[3]

## Summary

The emphasis in this introductory chapter has been upon the role of data communications in the task of moving information. Greater breadth in the design of business information systems is being facilitated by the compatibility of processing and communications.

In succeeding chapters, data communications in business information systems will be discussed in relation to:

1. its role in an organization at several levels,
2. its suitability and adaptability in a number of corporate and management situations,
3. communication problems in information systems,
4. planning a data communication system, and
5. important, discernible trends in the use of data communications.

Detailed information on specific types of communication services and equipment can be found in the back of the book with references throughout the body of the text for those readers who wish to use this Supplementary Information Section.

### Discussion Questions

1. Define data communications and describe several specific working applications.
2. How are data communications and data processing related?
3. Discuss the differences between "data" and "information" as used in a business sense.
4. What role can data communications play to meet the increasing information needs of an organization?
5. In what ways can data communications be used by small businesses which may only have one location?

---

[3] James Morris, "Breaking Communications Bottlenecks," **SYSTEMS — The Magazine of Management Methods** (May/June, 1963), Page 10.

### Chapter II

# THE ROLE OF
# DATA
# COMMUNICATIONS

Human beings have been observing for a long time that the world seems to be steadily growing smaller. It is nevertheless undeniable that the pace of this apparent contraction has accelerated enormously within the past decade. The jet planes that now streak across our oceans may soon be doing so at two or three times the speed of sound.

Communications has played an equally important role in drawing all parts of the world closer together. Within less than a twelve-month period, millions of people were able to watch the Olympic Games in Japan, the inauguration of a President in the United States, and a state funeral in Great Britain without leaving the comfort of their own homes.

Data communications has also benefited greatly from the recent technological advances in the more general field of communications. The most significant developments in data communications have taken place in the United States, where it is more widely used than in any other country in the world. Data communication techniques are assuming an increasingly valuable role not only because of the speed with which they transmit information, but also because of their ability to cope with the expanding volume of information generated by our society.

### The Information Explosion

Throughout most of man's history almost all knowledge was transmitted from mouth to ear, and then usually lost. The infinitesimal amount of information that was recorded was chiseled on stone or scrawled on parchment for others to read. But with the development of printing, man began the process of accumulating knowledge rapidly and disseminating it widely.

By 1800, it is estimated, the sum of human knowledge was doubling every fifty years. Then, in the 1830's came the full impact of the industrial revolution. It accomplished more than just the substitution of machines for human hands; the industrial revolution also gave birth to the information explosion. Information began to accumulate rapidly not only because the new machines were generating information, but also because man, freed to a large extent from the burden of manual work, was able to generate more information himself.

By 1950, the sum of human knowledge was doubling every ten years, and there were predictions that knowledge would continue to expand at such a rate that by 1970 it would be doubling every five years. Noting the trends, American scientists during the sixties warned of the problems that this mass and flow of information would produce. Dr. Vannevar Bush, a widely respected engineer and mathematician, cautioned that science might soon be strangled by its own product. By 1963, in the natural sciences alone, 600,000 technical documents were being published yearly, and it was clear that there would be a continuing acceleration in the amount of published scientific matter.

The effects of the information explosion were experienced in other areas of the economy. In medicine, for example, the dean of the medical school at the University of California in Los Angeles declared that more medical research had been published since World War II than in all prior human history. An executive of an aircraft company revealed that just the paper required for the design drawings of a jet plane outweighed the plane itself.

As knowledge accumulates, it becomes increasingly difficult for anyone to have access to all the information available in even a highly specialized field. Accordingly, the techniques of processing, filing, storage, and retrieval assume added significance in man's efforts to avoid the waste of duplicating work that someone else has already done.

Part of the answer to the retention and retrieval problem created by the information explosion lies in the use of computers as storage units. All the information related to an area of study can be stored in memory units associated with one or more computers. But even when existing information is stored in computer memory units, it is useful only if those seeking answers can gain rapid access to it. Easy and rapid access to computer-stored information can be available through data communications. An ultimate solution to the information problem may require the establishment of national libraries available to subscribers through remote-inquiry devices. Such inquiry devices linked to computers by communication channels would permit a user to key an inquiry into a machine and receive in return a visual display, a printed document, or an audible answer to his question. (*Figure 2.*)

### Data Communications as an
### Aid to Government

**National Defense.** The defense of our country depends upon what is undoubtedly the largest combination of computer and data communication systems in the world. Individual systems of the

Figure 2. Computers can automatically index and store information about specific fields of knowledge. Access to the information can be provided by remote inquiry terminals connected to the computer by data communication channels.

Department of Defense supply up-to-the-second command, control, and warning information (including detection, surveillance, and retaliation) required by the various unified and specialized commands of the Army, Navy, and Air Force. Individual voice and data communication networks may function in combination with one another as well as separately; they may be directly or indirectly tied together while serving one or several military commands. Most of these communication systems are provided by the communications common carriers.

A description of several of the more important systems may serve to illustrate the overall magnitude:

SAGE — One of the largest combined computer and data communication control systems in the world is the Semi-Automatic Ground Environment (SAGE) system operated by the Air Defense Command of the United States Air Force. SAGE is a surveillance and weapons control system that maintains watch over the skies of the North American continent. It is designed to receive information from the many radar sites including those from the CADIN (Canadian Integration North, formerly Pine Tree) systems, as well as from flying observation aircraft and ocean picket ships. Information from the various outposts is transmitted to central computers over data communication channels. The computers process the data and display pertinent information on special screens and radar scopes in military headquarters where it is evaluated by the Air Force personnel who monitor the system. As unidentified aircraft approach or violate United States air space, command personnel can be notified immediately and, if necessary, issue orders to dispatch and control interceptor aircraft or activate other weapons of the air defense system.

The dependence of the SAGE system on data communications is based on the fact that most of the radar sites in North America are located hundreds of miles from their central computers. With communication lines providing the primary link, information relating to these locations is transmitted to and from the control centers as events occur. Electrical communications satisfy the critical need for accuracy and reliability in the transmission of information vital to the security of the country.

SACCS (Strategic Air Command Control Systems) — This is a gigantic two-way communication system funneling information into SAC headquarters and sending operational instructions and commands outward to the force. Information concerning individual base readiness, bombers, missiles, tankers, personnel, etc., is converted into digital data and transmitted at speeds up to 3000 words per minute over communication lines to a central computer. Some information is continuously displayed by converting the computer language into conventional language, rapidly printing on a film and projecting in color on large screens. Virtually any information stored in the computer can be called up by the SAC commander as he desires.

BMEWS (Ballistic Missile Early Warning System) — Long-range radars in Alaska, Greenland, and England transmit ballistic missile and satellite tracking data to computers in Colorado Springs, Colorado. Voice and data circuits are used between Colorado Springs and each site. The communication facilities of the DEW Line and new under-ocean cables are also used.

SPADATS (Space Detection and Tracking System) — Computers at Bedford, Massachusetts, and Colorado Springs, Colorado, keep accurate, up-to-the-minute records of every orbiting object in space — payloads as well as pieces of "space junk" that accompany satellites into orbit. Tracking stations — radars and optic trackers — forward observations and tracking information to a SPADATS computer over communication lines. Anticipated orbits are calculated by the computers and anticipated tracks are transmitted back to the reporting stations for verification. The two computers are also connected by communication lines so that both may be continuously kept up to date. Radars of the BMEWS also supply satellite tracking information to SPADATS.

**Switched Networks** — In addition to special systems such as those mentioned above, the Departments of the Army, the Navy, and the Air Force share a sophisticated private automatic switched voice network (with data transmission capabilities) similar in operation to but separate from the Direct Distance Dialing network used by the public; and also a private automatic switched digital network with message switching[1] capabilities. These systems perform extremely important tactical service during periods of emergency; in non-emergency periods they are used to carry on normal routine and administrative matters.

**Federal Agencies.** The Federal Government utilizes several very large data communication networks in addition to those that have

---

[1] The concept of message switching is explained in the Supplementary Information Section.

military applications. The United States Weather Bureau, for example, uses an extensive network to collect and disseminate weather information to the Federal Aviation Agency, commercial airlines, agricultural organizations, and the general public. The National Aeronautics and Space Administration employs another large communications network for data acquisition and tracking in connection with its manned space vehicles and other space probing activities. The Federal Aviation Agency, the Veterans Administration, and the Social Security Administration have each established an extensive communications complex for transmitting both voice and data between their various locations.

**Law Enforcement.** Federal and State law enforcement agencies employ more than 200,000 people. The sheer size of this operation demands that law enforcement organizations utilize many of the most advanced techniques of business information systems, including the latest in data communications.

Rapid communications and ready access to records are essential to successful law enforcement. To complicate the problem, law enforcement activities in the United States are divided among a multitude of state, county, and municipal organizations that are highly interdependent for information and assistance. Furthermore, if law enforcement is to be effective, information must flow from the operational levels of each organization to the operational levels of the others. The faster a report of a stolen car can be sent from the desk sergeant in a city precinct to a county highway patrolman in the next state, the greater the chances of apprehending the thief and recovering the car.

Many states today have installed extensive teleprinter[2] networks to send administrative messages as well as reports of suspects, reports of stolen property, etc. These networks are interconnected with those of other states to exchange information rapidly throughout the country. Within minutes after initial receipt of word concerning a crime, relevant information can be distributed over a wide area, records checked, facts verified, and appropriate instructions issued.

Emerging trends in law enforcement indicate even greater dependence on data communications in the future. The tendency toward regional consolidation of law enforcement services, the automation of police information systems, and the establishment of regional record centers all herald an increase in the use of data communications.

---

[2] Teleprinter equipment is discussed in the Supplementary Information Section.

### Data Communications and the Firm

In the American economy, every business firm must be a dynamic entity always in a state of transition. It either advances or declines; it cannot stand still. This constant change in a company's status creates operational problems. The mark of an effective manager is his success in identifying problems and solving them with whatever means are available. Communications, as one of the available tools, plays a significant role in keeping a company in touch with its own divisions as well as with its customers and suppliers.

As companies become larger, more widely dispersed, and more diverse in their operations, and at the same time try to render better service at lower prices, the problems of internal communications become much more complex.

**Communications Links Newly Merged Firms.** The lure of reduced administrative costs, tax benefits, and an expanded base of operations has led to an unprecedented number of company mergers in the past few years. Although there are obvious advantages to such mergers, they are not without their problems. Physical consolidation of plants is often impracticable because of considerations such as existing union contracts, proximity to suppliers, and unexpired leases. Thus the rapid exchange of operating information becomes a vital consideration. Data communications can play a prominent role in bridging the gap in time and space between the merged companies.

If both firms have been using data processing equipment before the merger, it may be advantageous to devise a system that permits the companies to share the facilities. It is thus often possible to eliminate part, if not all, of the data processing equipment at one location. With data communications, the two companies can centralize all their data processing equipment or, at least, distribute the load between the two installations if both remain in operation. *(Figure 3.)*

Mergers permit many cost-cutting measures, including the sharing of some staff services. Close administrative cooperation is of paramount importance. Here, too, data communications can serve to link the two companies.

**Communications Improves Efficiency.** A corporation must examine many factors before deciding to transfer all or part of its operations to a new location. In our competitive, open economy, successful companies seek every opportunity to cut expenses and improve service. One way to achieve these goals is to move closer to available sources of labor and raw materials. Another is to move

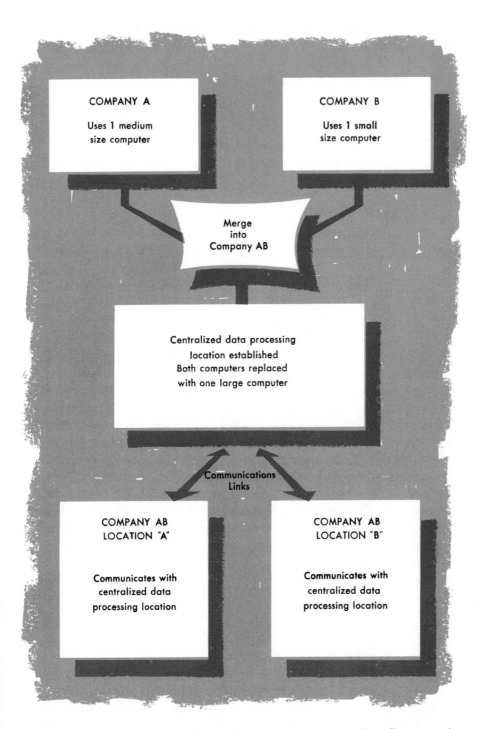

Figure 3. Even though two newly merged companies must remain physically separated, they can both have access to a new centralized data processing center through the use of data communications.

closer to the principal market area for the particular products. A third is to choose locations where building costs and taxes are lower or where labor costs can be reduced. While these objectives are sound reasons for moving to new locations, the resultant changes are almost certain to increase the problems of coordination.

An example of just such a situation may be seen in the case of a company that divided its manufacturing operations so as to produce television cabinets in one plant and the sets in another. Because of poor coordination between the two plants, inventories were almost continuously unbalanced. For some models, more cabinets than necessary were being produced, while in other cases there were not enough cabinets. This imbalance created additional expense and inconvenience; it became necessary, on occasion, to find temporary storage facilities for the surplus cabinets, even to the extent of using the barns of local farmers. Top management was unaware of the dimensions of the problem until an investigation was touched off when a customer complained of finding barnyard debris in the bottom of his television console. It was subsequently discovered that the breakdown in plant coordination had cost the company a substantial portion of the profits it might normally have expected to make.

Coordination of the supply of components required to manufacture a particular product is basically a problem of inventory management and production control. Whether the requirements are relatively simple, as in the case just cited, or involve the control of a great many parts manufactured or warehoused in widely separate locations, data communications can help to coordinate interplant activities. With effective communications, centralized control can be exercised over the rate of manufacturing of the various components. It is practical, moreover, to use data communications for rapid reordering of parts from outlying warehouses. When daily records of warehouse shipments are sent to the factory, it is possible to deliver (often by the next day) enough stock to replenish the inventory supply. This type of coordination limits the amount of stock required in the warehouse and thus reduces both the storage problem and the inventory cost.

**Communications Permits Larger Markets.** Many companies, no longer willing to depend upon one or two major products to supply the bulk of their sales revenue, are branching out into broader product lines. They are also attempting to find new markets for existing products.

Promotion of an existing product line by increasing its channels of distribution introduces a host of marketing and communication problems. A good example is the new trend in the marketing of children's clothing, for which the traditional retail outlets have always been department stores, large clothing chains, and children's apparel shops. In recent years, however, these products, individually wrapped in plastic bags, have been sold in increasing quantities in supermarkets.

A manufacturer cannot distribute products to supermarkets through the same channels he uses for department stores. Utilizing these supplementary channels of distribution requires changes in methods of placing orders, delivering merchandise, billing, etc. Stocks retained in supermarkets are limited and usually require more frequent reordering. Orders tend to be smaller and must be delivered faster to avoid shortages. In brief, these differences demand different types of communications.

**Communications Increases Services to Customers.** Customers in today's competitive climate are demanding and getting more service. They are no longer content to wait long periods of time for delivery of products. They want fast delivery, low prices, and firm commitments. A supplier who cannot provide these services is likely to lose his customers to a competitor who can.

Timely delivery is often the most valuable service a supplier can render. The faster a customer can expect delivery of an order, the smaller the shelf inventory he will have to maintain. Inventory can be further reduced if the supplier is willing to accept frequent small orders. Some form of automated ordering is also a help to a customer, for then he can prepare orders with a minimum of clerical effort. After one company had instituted an automated ordering system, it discovered that its annual sales to one of its customers increased from a previous average of $750 to almost $42,000 in the first year and to almost twice that in the following year.

The key to an automated ordering system is the conversion of order information into machine language (e.g., punched or marked cards, or paper or magnetic tape) as quickly as possible, preferably at the initiating customer's location. Using some type of communication service, the information can be immediately relayed to the supplier in machine-processable form. The order can be processed without delay, permitting much faster delivery.

In businesses such as banks, travel bureaus and airlines, which deal primarily in service, data communications can be used to obtain information quickly and to expedite transactions involving deposits and withdrawals or ticket and hotel reservations.

**Communications Reduces Operating Costs.** As competition forces prices down and labor and material costs continue to rise, profit margins tend to shrink. When this happens, managers look to the reduction of operating costs as a means of exercising economies.

Communications can serve in many ways to reduce operating expenses. Businesses that have decentralized plant operations in order to save transportation costs, often find it more economical to handle payroll, purchasing, billing, and other functions on a centralized basis. With the aid of data communications, all branch timecards, invoices, bills, etc., can be processed at a central location, reducing clerical costs at each of the plants. *(Figure 4.)*

Operating expenses can be reduced indirectly by accelerating the rate of processing invoices. Rapid receipt of orders in the accounting center expedites customer billing, and any reduction in the time gap between shipping and billing dates correspondingly lessens the "float" in accounts receivable. A decrease in that portion of working capital devoted to carrying customer accounts produces in turn a saving in interest charges.

### Data Communications and the Manager

The previous section discussed some of the ways in which data communications can be useful in the various aspects of a company's operations. Although installation of any of the systems described is a management decision, once the system becomes operational it functions much like any other part of the company's structure. Data communications, however, can also serve the business manager as a continuous tool, helping him to evaluate all relevant factors in his task of administering and managing the men, the machines, and the money available in his organization.

**Communications Permits Organizational Flexibility.** A one-man business has no need for internal communications. But as soon as the entrepreneur hires a secretary to help with office work, a communication requirement is established. In a two-room office, an intercom may serve as one link between secretary and employer. As the organization grows, so do its communication requirements; the more people engaged in the operation of the business, the greater the need for internal communications.

The primary purpose of organizational planning is to improve the ability of a business to conduct its affairs. The only justification for any form of internal organization is that it most effectively satisfies the particular requirements that called it into being. Until recently, the forms of organization available to many companies were limited by their requirements for intracommunication. A firm that needed timely, accurate information to operate efficiently had to keep its divisions relatively close to one another if management decisions were to be reached with dispatch. The available types of communications to a large extent determine the physical layout of the organization.

Today, however, as a result of advances in the science of electrical communications, business executives can be located completely in accordance with the needs of the organization. It is now practicable to send information anywhere in the nation, in almost any form, with accuracy and speed. In a matter of a few minutes, a sales

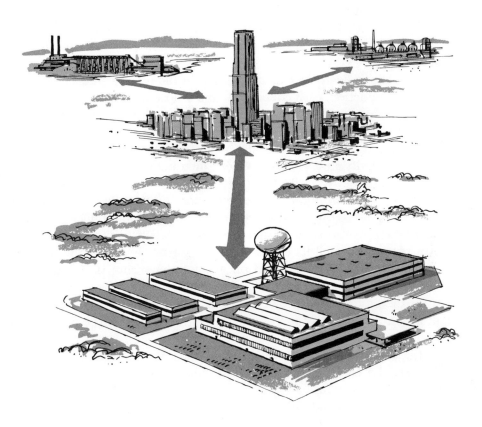

Figure 4. A company with several widely scattered operating locations can centralize the data processing function and make it available to all the locations through the use of data communications.

report, financial statement, or production report can be transmitted wherever needed so that a decision may be based on timely information. Through the use of advanced communication techniques, a company can determine its geographic distribution solely on the basis of the demands of the business. Plant proximity is no longer a prerequisite for reliable communications.

**Communications Improves Planning and Forecasting.** Planning and forecasting are by definition concerned with the future. But the basis of good planning is an accurate knowledge of the past. The more current and accessible the information about the past, the more valuable it becomes as a tool for planning. If a manager uses sales data that is one month old as a basis for planning the next month's sales program, he may be missing important information about events that occurred within the preceding week or two. Such information is especially critical when seasonal or perishable merchandise is handled. A sudden slump in sales could create stockpiles of unsalable items, while a sudden spurt in sales could deplete inventories and result in lost sales in the future.

Data communications can deliver up-to-the-minute information on sales, production, cash collections, and a host of other items — information that is vital to proper planning and forecasting. For example, today's information on machine down-time, available manpower, and project priority could be instrumental in planning tomorrow's activity in a job shop where men and machines must be employed efficiently.

The construction industry, to cite one illustration, relies on workable plans and realistic schedules to meet deadlines. One large construction company uses data communications to collect job status reports from all its construction sites every Friday night. On Saturday, the data is processed on a computer, using the Critical Path Method[3] of Scheduling. The computer reschedules each job, figures the cost of each project to date, and predicts the final cost and profits based upon the up-to-date progress reports. The revised schedules are then airmailed to the job sites on Saturday afternoon, and the superintendents have them in hand Monday morning. In this case, the company employs data communications to assemble up-to-the minute information so that plans for the following week may be revised in the light of the preceding week's events. *(Figure 5.)*

---

[3] Critical Path Method is a method of planning a project so as to bring it to completion in the shortest time at least cost. For a detailed discussion of CPM see **Project Management and Control,** R. L. Martino, American Management Association, New York, 1964.

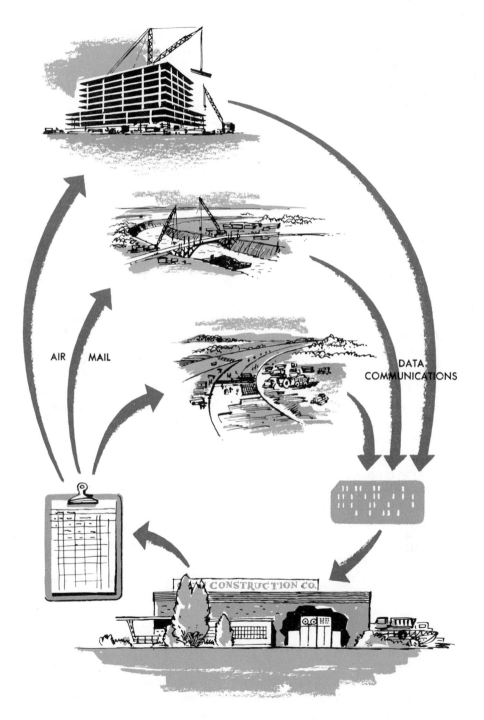

AIR MAIL

DATA COMMUNICATIONS

Figure 5. Status reports are transmitted to the construction company headquarters every Friday night. The data is processed and revised schedules prepared. The new schedules are airmailed to the project sites and arrive there Monday morning.

21

**Communications Improves Control.** The system just described is not only an example of an effective planning operation, but also an illustration of an effective control technique. In this sense, the company evaluates the latest information to determine whether the progress of each construction project is on schedule. In the Control Room at company headquarters are displayed all project information, architectural sketches, progress photographs, updated CPM (Critical Path Method) charts, and the company's current profit and loss picture. Each Monday morning, top management personnel convene in the Control Room to review each project and the company's position as a whole. If a project's time, cost or profit figures are significantly above or below estimates, steps are taken to determine the cause and start corrective action if necessary. In this company's system, data communications serves as a means of gathering timely information essential for centralized control of a far-flung operation.

**Communications Facilitates Decision Making.** Few things cause executives so much anguish as the need to make vital decisions before all pertinent information is available. Many types of decisions, of course, can be made on the basis of information days, weeks, or even months old, but others require an appraisal of factors that may change daily or even hourly. Without rapid communications, a manager may choose one course of action shortly after the entire framework of circumstances within which he must make the decision has changed.

Most large companies, for example, convert idle cash into United States Treasury bills as soon as possible to take advantage of the interest that can be earned. The most important information for the treasurer is the amount of cash available for investment. The critical time for decision making is the end of the day just before the money market is about to close. The more up to date the information about cash collections and disbursements, the more accurately the treasurer can decide how much cash to invest. If he has to delay the purchase until the next morning, the company will lose a day's worth of interest. When millions of dollars are involved, one day's interest amounts to a substantial sum of money.

If the company has an efficient data communication system, information about collections and disbursements anywhere in the country can be relayed almost instantaneously to the treasurer's office. At the end of each day, the treasurer can be sure that he has an accurate picture of the company's current cash position. He can thus make truly well-informed decisions as to whether he should buy or liquidate Treasury bills.

**Summary**

Advances in technology have enabled communications to play an increasingly important role as a tool of both government agencies and private business. As society becomes even more complex, corresponding progress in communication techniques will be required.

Communications is essential at every level of organization. The United States Government utilizes vast communication networks for voice as well as data transmission. Businesses also need communication systems to carry on their many complex operations. Communications helps companies disperse their operations without losses in efficiency. Managers of a business use communication channels for rapid access to the information required for daily decision. Thus overall planning and control can be based on information that is accurate, inclusive, and up to date.

## Discussion Questions

1. What problems has the "information explosion" created?
2. How do the uses of communications by law enforcement and military agencies provide examples for similar data communication systems in business?
3. How can business use data communications to improve efficiency?
4. How can top management use data communications to aid decision making?
5. Why is data communications important to the student of business administration?

### Chapter III

# D A T A

## COMMUNICATIONS

## IN MANAGEMENT

The previous chapters have stressed, mostly in broad terms, the variety of ways in which data communications can serve government and business. This chapter will consider the application of data communication techniques both to the various functional or departmental activities of a company and in an integrated information system for corporate management.

### Departmental Applications
### of Data Communications

Data communications can be useful in practically every area of business practice. Its range of application seems to be limited only by the ingenuity of system designers. Wherever dispersed sources of information present a problem, there is likely to be a role for data communications.

**Accounting Operations.** This area — usually one of the first to be automated when a company begins to install computers — was also among the earliest to receive the attention of data communication systems planners.

One large chemical company, for example, had used a system in which payroll information was recorded on time sheets at each of its four plants. These reports were mailed weekly and were received at company headquarters on Monday. Upon receipt of the time sheets at the accounting center, punched cards were prepared, the payroll was run on the computer, and the checks were printed out and sent to the main office for signature. The deadline for return mailing of the checks was 10 A.M. on Wednesday. The signed paychecks had to arrive back at the plants by Thursday for distribution to the employees. Adherence to the schedule was essential to good employee relations.

Although a payday had never been missed, the company was compelled on several occasions to charter planes to meet deadlines at two of its more distant plants. Because of delays in the method of transmitting time sheets, the company was unable to realize all the expected advantages of centralized processing.

After the situation was studied, it was decided to transmit time reports from each plant to the accounting center on the existing administrative teleprinter network. The reports were typed on a teleprinter and a punched paper tape was prepared. As the data was transmitted to the accounting center, it was converted directly to punched card form ready for immediate processing. Direct card preparation alone saved the company almost $500 a month in cost of keypunching and verification. The company was also able to complete its payroll processing twenty-four hours earlier, which provided a comfortable margin in meeting its deadline. The company plans to expand the system by transmitting payroll information to each plant where checks will be printed out automatically.

Another aspect of accounting procedure is illustrated by the case of a wholesale drug distributor. This firm maintained a separate billing operation at each of its warehouses so that an invoice could be packed with every order as it was shipped to the customer. The invoices were prepared from prepunched stock item cards. These cards were then trucked from the warehouses to headquarters for purposes of inventory control. Under this system, however, the inventory record in the computer was twenty-four hours old; consequently, the computer would frequently prepare orders that could not be filled from the specified warehouse.

A data communications system was established by which the prepunched cards for all orders received during the day (an average of 10,000 cards) are automatically transmitted every evening to the headquarters computer location.[1] The central computer prepares the invoices and determines whether all orders can be filled from standing inventory at the local warehouses. Items in short supply are requisitioned from the main warehouse and trucked to the local warehouses, together with the invoices, by 2 A.M. the following morning. This new system eliminates the need for accounting equipment at warehouse locations, improves the accuracy of the inventory record, gives the customers quicker and more reliable service, and saves substantial administrative expenses.

**Personnel Applications.** Most companies make every effort to maintain accurate, comprehensive employee records. Common to

---

[1] Punched card transmission terminals are discussed in the Supplementary Information Section.

almost all employee records are such basic facts as name, address, dependents, education, previous work experience, company work experience, and company training. Many companies, however, also record information of a more confidential nature, such as medical history, salary, and evaluations by supervisors. In the course of business, many people require access to the first category of information, but considerable difficulty could arise if the more confidential records were available just as freely. To provide the necessary security, some companies have established many different employee record centers, each containing only the information pertinent to the record centers' specific functions. In such an arrangement the basic information is duplicated at many locations. Also, because the information changes from time to time, there tend to be discrepancies among duplicate records at different locations.

A study of one company showed that employee records were being maintained at ninety different locations, that much of the information was duplicated at several locations, and that many of the records were not up to date. To cope with this problem, the company decided to consolidate all employee information in a computer center. Thereafter, when any division required personnel information, a teleprinter was used to interrogate the computer. The teleprinter would, in turn, print the computer's response. The computer would check the validity of the interrogator's confidential authority number before transmitting the information. After the information had served its purpose, the printed copy could be destroyed.

Such a system has several advantages: most of the space formerly required for storing records can be used for other purposes; employee information is more accurate and up to date; confidential information is available only to authorized personnel; and, last but not least, the savings in clerical expenses help offset the cost of the company's computer center and the associated data communication subsystem. The system, of course, is also available to perform many other data processing functions.

**Production.** A major problem among manufacturers is maintaining control over production lines. It is necessary to know at all times what raw materials have been used, how far each item has moved along the production line, how many items have been completed, and whether any bottlenecks have developed.

One large airplane manufacturer uses punched cards to identify every item used in the manufacture of a plane, ranging from material such as hydraulic fittings to pieces of sheet metal and barrels of bolts. As these items are issued from the supply room, the corresponding punched cards are transmitted to a computer.

The information is used to maintain an inventory of parts as well as to record the cost of each airplane. As inventories become depleted, the computer automatically issues orders for the purchase of more parts.

In another case, an automobile manufacturer uses a teleprinter network to send orders to various stations along the production lines. At each plant, detailed assembly instructions are prepared by data processing equipment for transmission over the teleprinter network. This system enables each station on the final assembly line and on the transfer lines feeding the final assembly lines to know exactly what is to be added to each car as it comes through. The first station on the line selects the desired basic body style. Subsequent stations are instructed as to type of tires, color of the interior, kind of radio to be installed, etc. The desired items are received as needed from the transfer lines, thus avoiding an accumulation of material at the final assembly stations. In this way, orders from all dealers can be coordinated and assembly line methods can be used to produce finished automobiles according to the specific wishes of each purchaser. *(Figure 6.)*

Figure 6. A teleprinter is used to receive assembly instructions at each station on an automobile production line.

**Marketing.** Electronic data processing has yet to achieve in marketing the status it holds in other areas of business operation. One reason for this is the pervading belief that marketing does not yield enough data to justify the use of a fair-sized computer. Many authorities point out, however, that the data does exist in great quantities but until now there has been no way to collect the information or to analyze it quickly enough to make it useful. The growing variety of terminal equipment coupled with data communications has now made it possible to collect marketing data rapidly and economically.

One large department store is installing a system that will include a communications link to report sales directly to a computer from cash registers in nine stores and a voice response from the computer when a clerk checks the credit standing of a customer. The computer will also provide management with a daily report on the cumulative sales of each department in every store compared to the equivalent period in the previous year, plus analyses of sales trends and even a report on the sales performance of each person on the selling floor.

One important aspect of marketing is the development of efficient sales procedures. Customers should be able to place orders easily, and their purchases must be processed quickly and accurately. Many companies have turned to data communications for solutions to their problems in these areas.

A wholesale hardware distributor, for example, has established a punched card system to permit customers to place their orders quickly and easily. Although the company stocks over 30,000 different items, most of its customers, the management learned, repeatedly requested the same items. To simplify the process, each customer was provided with a card-reader transmitting device and a supply of prepunched cards for the frequently ordered items. The cards contain the customer's number and the parts number. The ordering system works as follows:

1. When a customer wants to place an order, he telephones the distributor's card-punch receiving station.

2. Using the established telephone connection, the customer activates his card-reading device, which transmits the information contained on the chosen item cards. The desired quantity of each item is keyed in on a small keyboard associated with the card reader.[2]

3. The customer's cards are automatically duplicated at the distributor's receiving station.

---

[2] This punched card transmitting device is described in the Supplementary Information Section.

4. The distributor processes the duplicate cards to prepare a picking sheet to locate the items in the warehouse.

5. The order is assembled, checked, and sent to the customer, often on the same day it is placed.

Since this system was installed, orders from customers have increased substantially. Customers appreciate the arrangement, as it helps them reduce the size of their inventories and the costs of their purchasing operation. The system virtually eliminates paper work, since both customer and distributor can use the punched cards for computerized bookkeeping, and the order itself is prepared and transmitted with a minimum of preliminary paper work.

**Engineering Applications.** The complexities of engineering problems require that engineering and research people have access to data processing equipment; many types of complex problems are not readily solved with paper, pencil, slide rule, and desk calculator. In this area, too, data communications helps research and engineering personnel prepare and test new computer programs and transmit data over long distances.

A large chemical company uses teleprinters to prepare new engineering programs in punched paper tape form and to forward them to a large-scale computer at a data processing center. The engineer receives the results of the test of his program and returns any corrections to the computer via a keyboard printer. Engineers can also send their own data to the computer for processing. This system allows each engineer to have access to a computer for his own project assignments. It eliminates the need for a small computer at each of the engineering locations without any loss of time in research and development work.

An arrangement has been developed which allows several users to share a computer at the same time ("time-sharing"). Each user converses directly with the computer via a remote keyboard printer as he prepares his program. The computer analyzes the instructions as they arrive, and can send back error messages. This is called the conversation mode of operation. For engineering applications, it greatly increases the productivity of each engineer as compared to the older method with its inherent delays in getting a new program "debugged" and in running a problem on the computer. The conversation mode is discussed in detail in Chapter VI.

It can be seen from the foregoing examples that within the framework of business practice, data communications is widely used in conjunction with data processing equipment. Communication system designers can help management apply the economies of computer operations to every department of a corporation. So far, however, we have been considering each administrative subdivision — accounting, personnel, production, marketing, engineering — as more or less independent units. Perhaps the most dramatic example of the benefits data communications can provide is its capacity to help integrate all of the departments of a major company into a single coordinated system that permits both departmental independence and overall control in those areas that require it.

## Business Information Systems

*Figure 7* is a simplified representation of the way information flows in a Business Information System. Relevant information is accumulated from various operating sources, or from sources outside the company. After being processed, the data is acted upon, either directly by operating personnel in accordance with established rules, or analyzed by management so that appropriate action can be taken. All information that cannot be acted on at the lower levels is filtered out, and sent upward to the appropriate decision-making or action personnel.

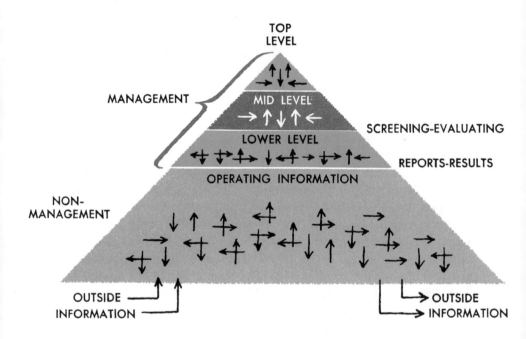

Figure 7. A Business Information System handles all of the company management and operating information. The operating information will generally represent the bulk of the information handled in the system.

It is apparent that the bulk of information handled is in the non-management area of the business. Such information includes factual, routine material essential to everyday operation: orders, inventory control, billing and purchasing. Operating reports and non-routine items move up the line to higher management. There is a corresponding downward flow of information designed primarily for the control of operations.

The apex of the pyramid represents the essential strategic knowledge required by top management — a distillation of the financial and operating data used for routine decisions at lower levels of the firm. In between the two strata, middle management is concerned with data for control of tactical operations, and, to some extent, with information for strategic decisions. Again the pattern reveals a lateral flow in addition to a downward flow of control information.

In Chapter I, a Business Information System was defined as a combination of people, data processing equipment, input/output devices, and communication facilities that supply the information needed to operate the business. In this definition input/output devices may be either remote data processing equipment or terminal equipment associated with communication links. In simplified terms, the three major elements of an information system are people, processing equipment, and communications. This combination can be envisioned as a three-legged stool, with the seat comparable to the information system itself. (*Figure 8.*) The three legs are reinforced with braces which in the analogy may be considered as aspects of systems planning.

When a Business Information System is analyzed in this way, the

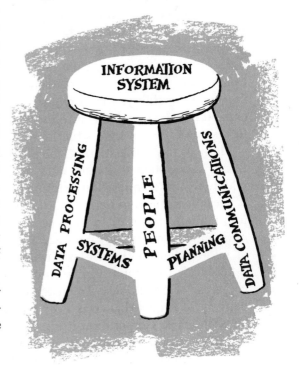

Figure 8. An information system is composed of data processing, data communications and people, supported by systems planning.

relationship between the various parts becomes clear. Any system design must consider all three elements; like a stool, it cannot stand on only two legs. The structural strength for the entire operation, then, is supplied by effective systems planning.

It will be useful to examine the Business Information System installed by the Westinghouse Electric Corporation. It demonstrates how designers can consider all the necessary elements of a complete system and establish a proper balance between them.

### The Westinghouse Information System

Late in 1962, Westinghouse established a corporate, general purpose information processing center using a high-speed, real-time[3] computer. This computer serves as the hub of a nationwide teleprinter network. The heart of the system is called the Tele-Computer Center.

Basic to the concept of the Tele-Computer Center is the use of the computer to perform the function of message switching in the network. The message switching activity, however, is a means to an end, rather than an end itself. With the computer as an integral part of the existing communications system, and with every message passing through it, it is ideally situated to identify and intercept data messages of many different kinds and to perform functions ranging far beyond the simple routing of traffic. In addition to its real-time capability, the computer has extensive batch processing capabilities, being arranged to interrupt batch programs in progress to take care of real-time situations.

Many of the applications involve the use of the real-time capabilities of the system to gather data via the teleprinter network from widely separated operations, storing it automatically, and processing it periodically as required for the production of management control information. Some of the applications result in the production of information for specific operating divisions, others in the production of information for the use of Headquarters management.

The Tele-Computer Center provides essential benefits in many key areas of operations. To customers, for example, it means faster delivery of orders than was ever possible before. To the Westinghouse Electric Corporation itself, it means more efficient operation and more valid information for management decisions. To Westinghouse salesmen it means greater speed in obtaining estimates, submitting quotes, and answering inquiries about stock availability, as well as improved service to their customers. (*Figures 9 and 10.*)

---

[3] The concept of "real-time" operation is discussed in Chapter VI.

The Tele-Computer Center serves approximately 300 locations throughout the United States and Canada. These include plants, administrative and sales offices, warehouses, repair centers, and distributors for the entire organization. The Tele-Computer Center has been designed to administer four major operations, each of which will be described briefly:

1. Message switching
2. Order processing and inventory control
3. Corporate accounting applications
4. Remote data processing

**Message Switching.** The first application of the information system, starting in December, 1962, was message switching, a function basic to the applications which were planned for later. In addition to performing various switching functions, the program takes care of a number of additional tasks, including generating daily statistics and message accounting. This message accounting is required for proper distribution of charges to the various company units using the communication facilities. Cards for billing are produced at the end of each day's run.

**Order Processing and Inventory Control.** Any of the 117 industrial and utility sales offices served by the information system may originate an order message, using a teleprinter to prepare a message tape in a specified format. The address code of the message directs it automatically to the order processing program within the computer.

The computer performs certain checking and editing functions and then proceeds to locate the desired items in its file of inventory records. If an item is out of stock at the warehouse nearest the customer, the computer searches for the item at warehouses progressively nearer the factory, and finally at the factory itself, in order to minimize transportation costs.

Having located the required items, the computer generates a message, directing the warehouses to ship the items. It also prepares the shipping labels, bills of lading, and packing lists for those items on the receiving teleprinters at the warehouses. Meanwhile price extensions and sales taxes have been calculated for the periodic invoice printing run. Inventory records are updated as each order is processed, and examined for reordering points. If a reordering point is reached, the applicable formulas are automatically brought

# FIGURE 9 THE WESTINGHOUSE TELEPRINTER MESSAGE SWITCHING SYSTEM

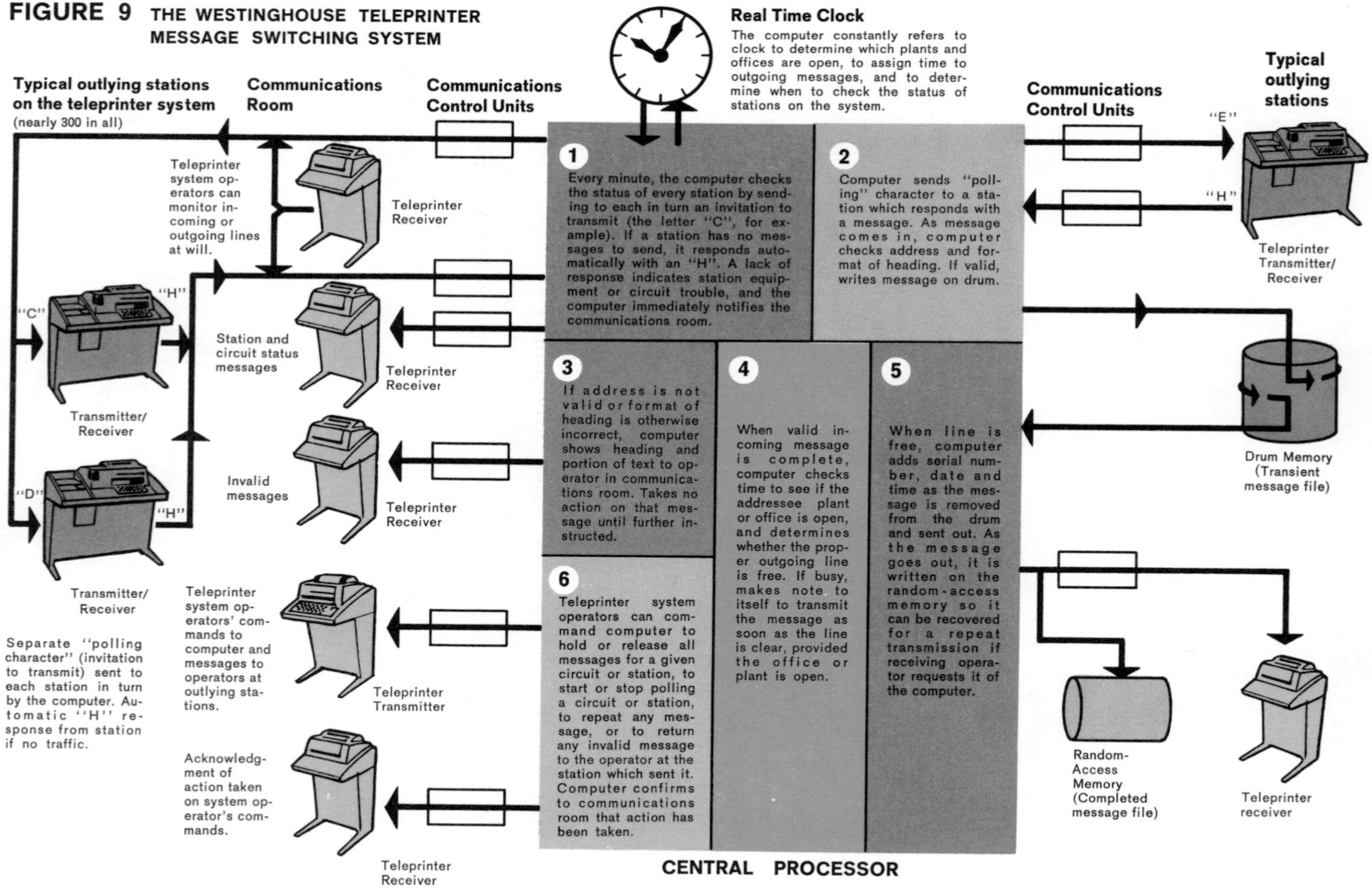

**Typical outlying stations on the teleprinter system**
(nearly 300 in all)

**Communications Room**

**Communications Control Units**

Teleprinter Receiver

Transmitter/Receiver "H"

Transmitter/Receiver "D"

"C"

Separate "polling character" (invitation to transmit) sent to each station in turn by the computer. Automatic "H" response from station if no traffic.

Teleprinter system operators can monitor incoming or outgoing lines at will.

Teleprinter Receiver

Station and circuit status messages

Teleprinter Receiver

Invalid messages

Teleprinter Transmitter

Teleprinter system operators' commands to computer and messages to operators at outlying stations.

Teleprinter Receiver

Acknowledgment of action taken on system operator's commands.

## Real Time Clock

The computer constantly refers to clock to determine which plants and offices are open, to assign time to outgoing messages, and to determine when to check the status of stations on the system.

## CENTRAL PROCESSOR

**① ** Every minute, the computer checks the status of every station by sending to each in turn an invitation to transmit (the letter "C", for example). If a station has no messages to send, it responds automatically with an "H". A lack of response indicates station equipment or circuit trouble, and the computer immediately notifies the communications room.

**② ** Computer sends "polling" character to a station which responds with a message. As message comes in, computer checks address and format of heading. If valid, writes message on drum.

**③ ** If address is not valid or format of heading is otherwise incorrect, computer shows heading and portion of text to operator in communications room. Takes no action on that message until further instructed.

**④ ** When valid incoming message is complete, computer checks time to see if the addressee plant or office is open, and determines whether the proper outgoing line is free. If busy, makes note to itself to transmit the message as soon as the line is clear, provided the office or plant is open.

**⑤ ** When line is free, computer adds serial number, date and time as the message is removed from the drum and sent out. As the message goes out, it is written on the random-access memory so it can be recovered for a repeat transmission if receiving operator requests it of the computer.

**⑥ ** Teleprinter system operators can command computer to hold or release all messages for a given circuit or station, to start or stop polling a circuit or station, to repeat any message, or to return any invalid message to the operator at the station which sent it. Computer confirms to communications room that action has been taken.

**Communications Control Units**

**Typical outlying stations**

Teleprinter Transmitter/Receiver "E"

Teleprinter Transmitter/Receiver "H"

Drum Memory (Transient message file)

Random-Access Memory (Completed message file)

Teleprinter receiver

# FIGURE 10 WESTINGHOUSE AUTOMATED ORDER PROCESSING AND INVENTORY CONTROL SYSTEM

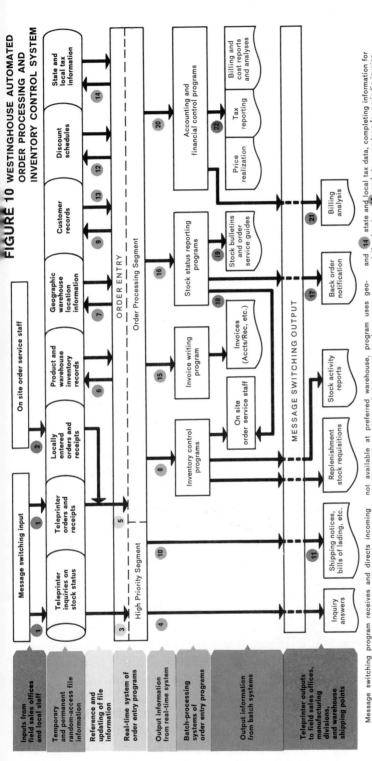

Message switching program receives and directs incoming messages:

(1) recognizes stock-status inquiries, customer orders, and stock receipt reports, and writes them on random-access section from which order entry program receives all job assignments. (2) On-site order service staff may receive messages via channels other than teleprinter. In such cases, they may enter information directly to the order entry program, by-passing the teleprinter switching input.

Stock-status inquiries receive priority: order-entry program (3) checks warehouse inventory for availability of ordered items at designated warehouse, or alternate warehouses, if necessary; and (4) replies in standard form through message switching output whose program also gives priority to stock-status messages.

Customer orders are processed as received. (5) They contain coded customer billing and shipping address, product identification, and preferred warehouse. (6) Order-entry program searches preferred warehouse inventory. (7) For items not available at preferred warehouse, program uses geographic warehouse file to find items at warehouses progressively closer to factory, and finally at factory itself.

(8) As items are assigned to an order, inventory totals are reduced accordingly. Inventory control program constantly monitors inventory records. When recording point is reached, program includes the item in daily inventory-control batch run which sends teleprinter stock-replenishment information to factories, calculated for economical production quantities.

Order-entry program performs shipment paperwork: order-entry program (9) extracts customer special requirements and shipping address from random-access file, and (10) sends shipping notices to selected warehouses via teleprinter switching output program. (11) Teleprinter at warehouses print the actual labels, bills of lading and all paperwork necessary to make shipment.

Order-entry program extracts from random-access file: (12) discount schedules for each item; (13) customer billing address and discount classification; and (14) state and local tax data, completing information for printing invoice (15) and stores on tape for periodic invoice-printing runs (several per day) and accounts-receivable input information.

If an item is out of stock: (16) the sales office and the customer are notified through daily back-order run, which also generates teleprinter notification (17) of back-ordered items; (18) order service staff at Tele-Computer Center is notified via printed reports, run several times daily. (19) Stock-status reporting program also generates weekly stock bulletins on active items, monthly stock statistics for manufacturing division planning, and a periodic order service guide to the entire product file.

At end of each day: (20) order-entry program initiates daily accounting and financial control program; (21) information for billing analyses is automatically collected for each manufacturing division; (22) price realization reports, tax reports, and billing-versus-cost reports and analyses are printed.

into play to determine the proper replenishment quantity. A requisition message is automatically produced and sent to the proper factory. Sales statistics are also accumulated during the processing of orders. The entire process takes less than three seconds after receipt of an order message.

The system provides as a by-product a high-speed, automatic stock inquiry service to sales offices. Priority is given to these inquiries; the only delay is the time necessary to complete the transmission of a message already in progress on the receiving line. Before installation of the system, information received by sales offices was often two to six weeks old.

**Corporate Accounting Applications.** The Tele-Computer Center also performs most of the corporate and headquarters accounting functions. Those for which time is not a critical factor are handled as conventional batch processing applications. Among such functions are the maintenance of stockholder records and issuance of dividends; maintenance of headquarters, regional and pension payrolls; generation of monthly budget statements; and maintenance of fixed asset records and depreciation accounting.

There are two major accounting programs which are run on a real-time basis. The output of these programs provides information that is of extreme interest to management, and the usefulness of this information for decision-making purposes declines rapidly with age.

One of these accounting programs is the gathering and compilation of month-end financial results from the profit centers and subsidiaries. At the beginning of 1964, Westinghouse abandoned the old method of gathering the month-end results of the profit centers by mail and manually auditing, correcting, and assembling the individual results into group and corporate statements. Now, on the appointed closing day, a real-time computer program gathers the trial balances of the profit centers via the teleprinter network, auditing each set of figures as it arrives. If discrepancies are discovered, a request for correction is generated by the program and automatically sent to the reporting location over the teleprinter network. When all locations have reported correctly, the key statements are immediately generated in final form for reproduction and distribution to top management. It is now possible, through the use of the teleprinter network, to speed up the receipt of the financial data and, with automatic auditing and assembly, to give this vital information to management several days earlier than in the past.

In July, 1964, the second of the major real-time accounting programs went into operation at the Tele-Computer Center. The cash management information program provides the company's Headquarters Treasury Department with complete and up-to-the-second data relating to cash. The teleprinter network is utilized for collecting data in the computer as well as for providing daily reports and answering specific inquiries from Treasury. The program includes the continuous recording of deposits of cash collections, the transfer of funds to cover the cash needs of the various divisional activities, the maintenance of bank balances for the approximately 250 bank accounts used by the company, and the reporting of cash data to Headquarters Treasury.

More importantly, this program demonstrates the feasibility of providing management with up-to-the-minute financial data by "push-button" request from a remote office. An inquiry device has been installed in the Treasury Office which enables that office to request such information as the up-to-the-minute cash position of the company, the amount of collections from customers, the disbursements made from the company's various payroll and accounts payable locations, the current balance in any of its bank accounts, the availability of such funds, and the current status of its marketable securities. The Treasury personnel merely set a few dials on the inquiry device and push the button — from then on, the communications network and the computer take over. The computer receives the inquiry, interprets it, and within a few seconds relays the answer back to the treasurer's office.

Also, the various divisions now have a new means of requisitioning funds to cover their disbursements. Each time the divisions issue checks to pay employees or suppliers, they send a teleprinter message directly to the computer. The computer extracts certain key information from the memory file and relays the message to a teleprinter at the local bank. Using this teleprinter message as its authority, the bank transfers funds from the local bank account to the appropriate division's bank account by way of the bank's wire service.

**Remote Data Processing.** With the computer tied into every company location large enough to justify a teleprinter terminal, each such location has direct access to the information-processing facilities of the Center. Westinghouse is now working on a pilot project to extend the capabilities of the information center to one of its manufacturing divisions. The program will provide the manufacturing division with an information processing and real-time information retrieval service it could not afford to support by itself. Thus, the Tele-Computer Center will eventually serve as a source of information not only for top management, but also for the managements of separate divisions in the internal operation of their businesses.

## Summary

The emphasis in this chapter has been upon the many possible business applications of data communications. Although only a few examples were described in detail, there is probably no area of a business operation that cannot use data communications effectively.

But this wide applicability of data communications can result in each department setting up its own data processing and communications system without regard to the needs of other departments. A company-wide approach to the data processing and communications problem, however, can result in a highly efficient Business Information System serving the needs of all departments. In many cases, the best solution is a center with data communication facilities serving all units of the organization. An example of such planning is the information system of the Westinghouse Electric Corporation.

### Discussion Questions

1. Describe two business examples to demonstrate the close working relationship between data communications and data processing.
2. Discuss the concept of a Business Information System.
3. Does the establishment of a Business Information System tend to increase or decrease the problems of internal record-keeping? Why?
4. How could one communication system be used to satisfy the needs of both the payroll department and the production department?
5. List four concrete benefits accruing to the Westinghouse Electric Corporation as a direct result of its Tele-Computer Center in Pittsburgh.

### Chapter IV

# COMMUNICATION PROBLEMS IN INFORMATION SYSTEMS

Recognition of a problem is always the first step toward finding a solution. As businesses, government agencies, and other large-scale organizations become increasingly aware of the potential of data communications, they are learning to look more critically at their existing systems of information handling. Problems that formerly were unrecognized or were considered among the unavoidable drawbacks of being large and having widely scattered operations are now being examined in the light of new knowledge in the field of communication techniques. As a company approaches unwieldy size, its management can consider decentralization with the assurance that it can link all its independent or semi-independent components to a central unified body with a communications system that speeds information from the point of origin to the point where it will be used.

Before an organization can utilize the techniques of data communications, it must first recognize not only the existence of a problem in information handling but also the type of problem. For purposes of discussion, it is useful to classify information problems into six basic categories. These are: Belated Information, Outdated Information, Inaccessible Information, Expensive Information, Inaccurate Information, and Mutilated Information. There is, of course, a certain overlap in these classifications — information that is outdated or inaccessible is necessarily belated — but solutions are easiest to find when the origin of the difficulty is pinpointed.

## Belated Information

Late arrival is the most common problem of information movement. One or two case studies will highlight the requirement for closer coordination in the transmission of information.

Because the first applications of electronic data processing were heavily slanted toward accounting functions, it is not surprising that, today, many firms process their entire payroll at one centralized location. This practice automatically creates a problem of getting the time-card information into the data processing center quickly and then returning paychecks to widely scattered locations in time to meet the pay schedules.

A solution is to devise a system which will convey time-card information from the plant site to the centralized accounting point in a matter of minutes. The United States mail or a fleet of messenger trucks can deliver payroll data covering most of the work days in a payroll period, but sending in the data for the last few days of the period may require a faster means of communication.

A wood products company that operates several lumber camps in the Pacific Northwest had just such a problem. Like the chemical company discussed under *Accounting Operations* in Chapter III, this company found it difficult to get time-card information from the camp sites to the data processing location, prepare the paychecks, and return them in time to meet the loggers' payday. The problem was solved by using a teleprinter and a teleprinter exchange service[1] to transmit the time report to the main plant at the end of each week. *(Figure 11.)* After the payroll is processed and the paycheck information calculated, the main office calls each lumber camp, using the same communication service. The payroll clerk at the lumber camp inserts special paycheck forms in the keyboard printer, which then automatically prints the paychecks from the data being sent from the main office. An authorized official at each camp signs the checks. This system has reduced payroll processing time to such an extent that paychecks can include wages for the previous working day.

In another situation, a telephone company owned a series of storerooms scattered throughout the state. Each of these storerooms daily ordered materials, which were required for the following day, from a central warehouse. The material requirements were not usually known until late in the afternoon, and by the time requisitions were completed and sent to the central warehouse, it was impossible to make deliveries the following day.

To solve this time problem, each storeroom was provided with a small desk-top punched card transmitter and a set of prepunched cards, one card for each frequently ordered item. During the evening, after the order has been determined, the stockroom attendant at each of the storerooms places a telephone call to establish connection with the card punch at the central warehouse. He identifies his location and authenticates his order by means of a prepunched card containing the number of the storeroom and his authority

---

[1] Teleprinter exchange services are described in the Supplementary Information Section.

Figure 11. A wood products company uses teleprinters to send timecard information from the lumbering camps to the data processing center. The same machines are used later to receive the payroll information on paycheck blanks which are then signed by the camp manager.

number. He then feeds in, one at a time, a punched card for each item of the order. The quantity of each item is entered manually by means of a small keyboard associated with the punched card transmitter. As this information is transmitted, it is punched into a card at the warehouse.

After the cards are punched at the warehouse, they are processed on a computer that produces a printed requisition. In addition, the computer handles the billing and inventory control tasks. Soon thereafter, the order is filled, the appropriate truck is loaded with the shipment for each storeroom, and delivery is made during the early morning hours of the following day. *(Figure 12.)*

In this example, data communications permitted delivery time to be reduced by one day, making it possible to keep inventories to a minimum and, at the same time, to fulfill the needs of customers more rapidly.

**Outdated Information**

Most companies possess a great deal of information in one form or another. But even when much of this information is maintained

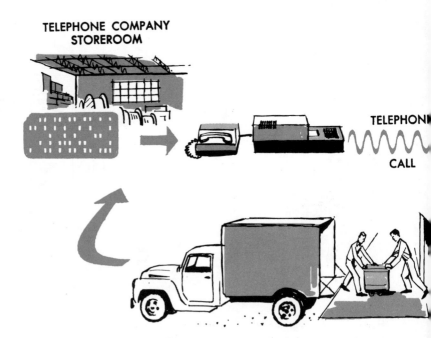

TELEPHONE COMPANY
STOREROOM

TELEPHONE
CALL

Figure 12. Some telephone companies use punched card systems to order materials from the supplier's warehouses.

in some machine-processable form such as paper tape, punched cards, or magnetic tape, the latest information is often not available to many of the people who need it.

Many gas, electric and telephone companies, which usually bill their customers monthly or bimonthly, have such a problem. Although most utility companies have automated and centralized their billing procedures, they frequently accept incoming payments at many widely dispersed points convenient to the consumer. In the absence of a data communication system to reconcile centralized billing with the decentralized accounts receivable operation, the computer at central headquarters does not have up-to-date payment information. It may send a delinquency reminder to some customers who have already paid their bills but whose accounts have not yet been credited.

Information that is unavailable to those who need it is of little value. For example, branch sales offices sometimes write orders contingent upon the company's ability to deliver. But many sales offices have no means of determining whether the factory or which of several warehouses can fill an order at the time it is being written.

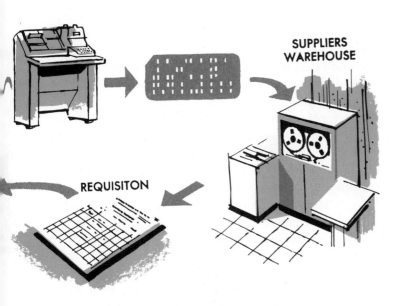

SUPPLIERS WAREHOUSE

REQUISITON

An appliance manufacturer was confronted with this problem. His sales offices required up-to-date information on the inventory status of the various appliances manufactured. The information was available in the computer center at the main office but was only sent to the sales office periodically. As a result, many important customers had not received their orders as promised. The situation demanded attention.

An appraisal of the problem revealed the advantages of giving each sales office access to the information in the computer. A system was designed that enabled a salesman in any of the offices to immediately determine the availability of a particular appliance model. The salesman would place a teleprinter call from his office to the computer, which would then search its "files" and send back the information in printed form on the salesman's teleprinter. If the order was entered at the time of inquiry, the sale was entered in the computer memory and the computer revised the inventory on hand accordingly. With this system the company not only extended the services of its computer to the branch sales offices but also was able to keep its inventory file up to date.

When a company's operations are dispersed, it is inevitable that information frequently has to be transferred from one location to another as needed. Data communications can provide this mobility.

### Inaccessible Information

Essential day-to-day operating information may be located in places inaccessible to ordinary means of data collection. Perhaps the points where information must be gathered are so scattered, so numerous, or so remote that it is difficult to reach them all. In most cases, data communications can help to overcome problems of information inaccessibility.

A problem of this type confronts state authorities responsible for maintaining the purity of rivers and streams. In many cases, water pollution is caused by industrial wastes dumped into the streams. One aid to controlling pollution is daily monitoring of the various streams to check on the purity of the water. In this way, it is possible to detect quickly any pollution-producing wastes that have been deposited in the streams. However, a genuinely effective system of control requires frequent monitoring of all locations where wastes might be dumped into the water. It would be prohibitively costly to maintain such a system solely on the basis of manpower.

One practicable solution is to establish monitoring devices at appropriate points along each stream. These devices, already commercially available, can check such conditions as turbidity, temperature, percentage of dissolved oxygen, and degree of acidity. The devices can be connected to regular telephone lines in the same way that home telephones are connected to the nearest telephone switching office. The central testing bureau can then call each of these remote monitoring devices, perhaps as often as every fifteen minutes, and automatically read out and record the various test measurements. In this way, it is possible to maintain a close check on the purity of the water at many locations and know very quickly where pollution has occurred. With such a system, it is also possible to periodically move these monitors from one location to another. This periodic movement gives the system greater scope and permits it to cover a very large area on an intermittent basis.

A similar problem is associated with the Nuclear Test-Ban Treaty of 1963. Some scientists regard the effectiveness of the ban on nuclear testing in the atmosphere as directly proportional to the adequacy of our own devices for detecting changes in the earth's magnetic field. (Any nuclear explosion in the atmosphere will cause a change in the earth's magnetic field.) One research group advocates establishing a worldwide system for monitoring the strength and direction of the earth's magnetic field. To avoid electrical interference, the basic measuring devices (called magnetometers) must be placed in remote locations miles from any highway or road, or even from any television transmitting antenna. Telephone lines can be used to transmit readings from the unmanned devices directly to a centralized computer.

The two examples cited relate to problems of gathering information from remote locations. Many of the problems engendered by the information explosion discussed in Chapter II also fall into the "inaccessibility" classification. In most cases, data communications can help to provide a workable solution.

**Expensive Information**

The storage and maintenance of the same customer information at more than one place can prove to be an expensive practice. Local branch offices and agencies of insurance companies, for example, have customarily kept policy information on those clients whom they service, recording changes as they occur and forwarding the information to the home office. Some companies, however, have found it more economical to store all policy information in a computer center at the home office. All premium notices are sent from the home office.

Whenever a branch office or agency requires information from a policy of one of its clients, it uses a teleprinter to place a call to the computer at the home office. The computer searches its memory and prints out all the requested information on the terminal equipment located in the local office. Any changes first recorded in the local office can be routed to the home office with the same equipment. Thus, it is not necessary for each local office to maintain a complete file of such information as the status of policy loans and premium payments, most of which might not be up to date. Neither is it necessary for the home office, which administers all policies on a current basis by means of its computer, to send the branches all policy status information, much of which might never be needed.

Any situation that requires maintenance of identical information at both central and subsidiary locations warrants reappraisal in the light of the ability of data communications to transmit data without significant delay from a central storage location to wherever it is needed. It will often be found that costs can be lowered substantially by eliminating duplicate local files, not only because of the duplicate work of maintaining the file and the additional cost of record storage, but also because of the problem of reconciling discrepancies which tend to arise.

### Inaccurate Information

Frequent complaints about the accuracy of orders and other data that must pass through several processing locations indicate another problem in the movement of information. One typical case will illustrate the point.

A steel manufacturer presently has orders typed in the sales office, with copies sent to the originating salesman, the district sales office, and the central sales order section. The sales order section reviews the order, adds to it the mill order number, scheduling data, and the credit rating and then prepares a new eleven-part order form to send copies to various departments in the mill: production control, shipping, traffic, statistical center, and billing.

As the separate copies of the order are processed through the plant — for example, from shipping to traffic and back again — any new information supplied by one department must be added to other copies of the same order at different locations. The opportunities for error in such a system are manifold. In fact, many costly omissions of information and inaccurate entries do occur.

To help correct these problems, a data communication system is being planned that will not only transmit the information accurately, but will reduce the number of times the same material has to be recopied. For example, teleprinter equipment can produce a punched paper tape in which all the original data is recorded, e.g., customer's shipping and billing addresses, item and quantity ordered, etc. A rerun of the tape at any time results in page copy identical to the original order and in the same format. Because only the new information has to be added manually, the opportunities for human error are greatly diminished. In addition, the routing time of order copies is reduced, as plant messenger service is replaced by data transmission links.

## Mutilated Information

Some university clubs in the larger cities have a large membership and operate extensive club facilities. To cite a specific case, one university club in New York City has over 1,800 members. Their individual expenditures at the club are recorded on "chits" (signed vouchers covering expenditures). Under the former system, the chits were collected on a daily basis from the various departments — restaurant, barber shop, lodging, etc. — manually sorted by clerks in the main office, and then forwarded to an outside service bureau for billing and other processing. Bills were printed by the service bureau computer and returned with the chits to the club for mailing.

Because of frequent handling for assembling, processing and two-way mailing, many chits were hard to read and too many errors were being made. Furthermore, members' questions about specific charges could not be answered while the chits were at the service bureau.

When consulted about this problem of mutilated information, representatives of the communication and business-machine companies recommended the use of an adding machine equipped with a tape punch for the production of a punched paper tape. The club installed the equipment. Now all chits are gathered daily and an operator keys the account number, a code number to identify the kind of charge, and the amount. The punched paper tape is sent to the service bureau daily by means of teleprinter equipment. This new system eliminates the necessity for repeated handling of the chits and solves the problem of mutilated information.

## Summary

The information-handling system of a company should be examined whenever significant information flowing through the system is belated, outdated, inaccessible, expensive, inaccurate, or mutilated.

The significance of such a problem does not necessarily relate to the frequency with which it occurs. Even an occasional difficulty may develop into a major problem if it affects service to important customers. Business managers are well advised to be alert to such warning signs and to institute a remedial program before the problem becomes major.

## Discussion Questions

1. In your own words, describe the six basic classifications of information problems.
2. What other difficulties, not described in the text, might arise in connection with the movement of information?
3. What are some of the probable consequences if information handling problems are allowed to remain uncorrected?
4. How can data communications help solve the problem of belated information?
5. What are some of the advantages of a centralized file with fast communication access over duplicate records at several locations?

### Chapter V

# PLANNING A
# DATA
# COMMUNICATION
# SYSTEM

The task of planning a data communication system is best approached as a problem requiring the application of scientific method. As with any such problem, a solution is found most readily by following certain logical steps. These steps can be summarized as follows:

(1) Identify and define the problem.
(2) Gather and analyze the facts.
(3) Develop alternative solutions.
(4) Test solutions to determine their effectiveness and efficiency.
(5) Select best solution.
(6) Implement the solution.
(7) Follow up.

In applying this method to the problem of designing a data communication system, it is useful to restate these steps in more specific, goal-oriented form:

(1) Identify and define the problem describing the objectives to be sought from improved data communications.
(2) Gather and analyze the facts to determine the specifications for:
   (a) Distribution,
   (b) Volume,
   (c) Urgency,
   (d) Language,
   (e) Accuracy of the information.
(3) Design alternative data communication systems that will meet both the specifications and the objectives.

49

(4) Determine costs of the alternative systems.

(5) Evaluate all systems in relation to:

    (a) How well they meet the objectives,

    (b) How well they satisfy the specifications,

    (c) How much they cost,

    (d) What other benefits they provide,

    And select the best solution.

(6) Implement the selected system.

(7) Follow up:

    (a) To assure that system does indeed meet the objectives,

    (b) To determine if the requirements of the system have changed.

This chapter will discuss each of these steps in detail. Particular attention will be devoted to Step 2, for this is the area that demands the largest part of a communication system designer's time.

## Identify and Define Problem

Plans to use a data communication system result from either a need to solve a specific information handling problem or from a desire to explore the possibility of benefiting from the new communication techniques. Both motives are often present to some degree.

Problems that indicate a need for some improvement in information handling methods usually fit into one or more of the categories in Chapter IV (belated, outdated, inaccessible, expensive, inaccurate, and mutilated information). Even problems that are not immediately apparent tend to incubate, grow, and suddenly become urgent when customers begin to complain about such things as late deliveries or inaccurate bills. This kind of eruption can be avoided if a manager maintains a close watch over the flow of information within his company and is alert to warning signs that indicate possible problems in the movement of information.

Even though a problem seems to have been identified, the analyst must be certain that he is not treating just the symptoms rather than the problem itself. Errors in billing information, for example, can be minimized by having clerks recheck each bill, but even though the incidence of error may be greatly reduced, the basic cause of error (perhaps handwritten orders that are difficult to read) will not have been eliminated.

It is also essential that the objectives of the new system be clearly stated. They will be the guidelines for design of the system and will also supply the standards by which it can be measured. The objectives should be stated in terms of the company's own particular operation. This list of general objectives incorporates most that are likely to apply to any specific company:

(1) Improve service to customers.
(2) Reduce costs of order handling, inventory, data processing, record keeping, or other company operation.
(3) Make more selective and relevant information available to management.
(4) Reduce the time delay in payroll preparation.
(5) Provide an integrated information system serving all departments.
(6) Reduce inventories without delaying shipment of orders.
(7) Shorten the period required to prepare invoices.
(8) Reduce delivery intervals.
(9) Make data processing capabilities available to remote locations.
(10) Shorten the time required to determine stock availability in order to quote delivery dates to customers rapidly.

After the analyst has identified and defined the problem and has carefully set forth the objectives of the new system, he is in a position to take the next step in planning a data communication system.

## Gather and Analyze the Facts

In planning a data communication system, five major characteristics of the information to be moved must be considered. These characteristics are *distribution, volume, urgency, language* and *accuracy.* Each must be analyzed in detail, for upon them is based the whole design of the system.

**Distribution of the Information.** A logical starting point in the design of a data communication system is to determine the most efficient pattern for internal distribution of company information. The system designer should first make a chart showing all the locations that receive or provide such essential operating information as sales orders, production reports, payroll data, etc.

Such a chart might resemble the one in *Figure 13* which shows

| FROM \ TO | HEADQUARTERS | FACTORY | SALES OFFICE A | SALES OFFICE B |
|---|---|---|---|---|
| HEADQUARTERS | | Orders and production scheduling information | Administrative messages | Administrative messages |
| FACTORY | Shipment and production reports | | Order status | Order status |
| SALES OFFICE A | Orders | Inquiries on orders | | |
| SALES OFFICE B | Orders | Inquiries on orders | | |

Figure 13. A typical information flow for a small company with a headquarters, one factory and two sales office locations.

the information flow for a small company with a headquarters, one factory, and two sales offices. The chart also shows the type of information that is exchanged among the four locations. Notice that in this simplified example no information flows between the two sales offices. Although it may not be obvious here, the information sent between two locations will frequently move in only one direction.

An experienced communication system designer may also diagram the information flow on a map to show the geographical distribution. When locations are scattered over a wide area, it is helpful to see a schematic showing them in relation to one another. *Figure 14* is a geographical diagram for the company described above.

Most company information systems are of course more complicated than this example. However, means are available to aid in the analysis of larger systems since all distribution systems, no matter how complex, can be broken down into one or more of four basic patterns:

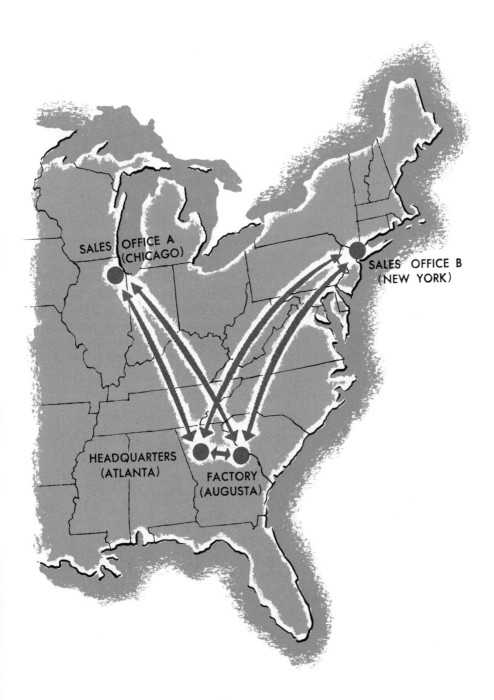

SALES OFFICE A
(CHICAGO)

SALES OFFICE B
(NEW YORK)

HEADQUARTERS
(ATLANTA)

FACTORY
(AUGUSTA)

Figure 14. By diagraming the information flow on a map it is often easier to see relation-ships between the locations that are not otherwise obvious.

1. One point to one other point.
2. One point to many other points.
3. Many points to one point.
4. Many points to many other points.

The phrase "many points," may refer to any number from two to several hundred or more. The more points, of course, encompassed by the distribution pattern, the more complicated the design problem. For purposes of illustration, "many" will be exemplified by an eight-point pattern. These various distribution patterns are illustrated in *Figure 15*.

The *one-to-one pattern* is very simple. The flow of information may be in one direction only, in either direction alternately, or in both directions simultaneously. In communications terms these directional flows are called one-way, half duplex, and duplex (sometime full duplex) transmission, respectively.

The choice of communications channel type depends upon the volume of data that will flow between the two points. If the volume is low, a dialed-up call between the two points will prove the most economical. On the other hand, if the volume between the two points is large, a private line obtained from a communications common carrier or from company-owned equipment may be more economical than dialed-up calls because it could be used twenty-four hours a day at a fixed charge.

The *one-to-many pattern* is used in systems where (1) information is disseminated to many locations from one centralized office, or (2) the centralized location initiates calls to outlying locations and the information is returned from these locations. An example of the first type is a weather broadcast network which sends out weather reports to many stations.

In the second type, the central location periodically calls each outlying office. Since the calls are made on a regular schedule, the personnel at each office know when to expect their calls and the operators can have their information ready for transmission when called. This reverse flow of information, however, does not change the basic *one-to-many* distribution pattern because the calls still emanate from one location.

The type of channels to be used in this system will again be determined by the volume of information to be transmitted. If the volume is great enough it may be necessary to extend private lines to each of the outlying locations. It would also be possible to make use of a special communications service which enables the central location to place dialed-up calls as often as necessary without affecting a predetermined flat-rate monthly charge.

54

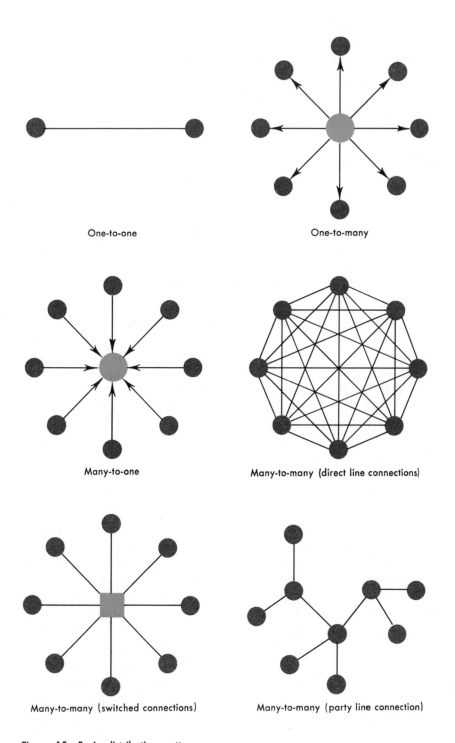

One-to-one

One-to-many

Many-to-one

Many-to-many (direct line connections)

Many-to-many (switched connections)

Many-to-many (party line connection)

Figure 15. Basic distribution patterns.

The third basic classification is the *many-points-to-one-point* pattern. As in the previous *one-to-many* pattern, it is the direction of calling which determines the distribution pattern. A typical case is an inquiry system where many locations call into a computer for information. In this case the desired replies flow outward from the computer in response to the inquiries.

In other cases, the direction of calling and the flow of information are the same. For example, sales offices may initiate calls to a centralized data processing center and transmit sales orders for further processing.

The *many-points-to-many-other-points* distribution is the most complex of the four basic distribution patterns. Every point in the system can send and/or receive information from every other point in the system. In *Figure 15,* the pattern is shown as if there were a direct line between each of the many points. This is the situation in which the early telephone companies found themselves when they tried to interconnect every customer with every other customer. This system soon proved to be uneconomical, and switching centers were established to provide temporary connections between the calling party and the party being called. This arrangement permits economical application of the basic distribution pattern of many points to many points. In this arrangement, every location is connected to the switching center via a direct line. When information is to be sent to any location, the calling station identifies (by dialing or using special address codes) the called station, and the switching center acts as the point of connection for the two lines. After the information has been transmitted, the connection between the two lines is broken.

There is one other method of interconnecting many locations so that any station can send or receive information from any other station. This method provides for the connection of all the stations on a party line arrangement. In its simplest version every message sent on the line is received at every location. It is possible, however, for each station to have its own special address code, and any station wishing to send a message can first send the *Call Directing Code*. This CDC will activate only the equipment located at the intended receiving station; all other stations will remain turned off. Only the proper station, therefore, receives the message. Again the basic distribution pattern of many-to-many has not changed even though the method of handling the information is different. This arrangement usually utilizes private lines to connect the stations.

In each of these basic distribution patterns, the volume of information to be handled is a significant factor. In a large communication system, variations in volume between the different points may dictate that more than one distribution pattern be employed.

A multiple arrangement is shown in the diagram of the communications network used by a two-division company. *(Figure 16.)* The Western division of this company contains a sub-system that requires a one-to-many distribution pattern. In this division, orders from all the sales offices are collected at one location. Since the volume of information at each location is relatively small, and there is no exchange of information between the sales offices, the offices can be called with dialed-up calls. The accumulated information is forwarded from the collecting sales office over a private line to company headquarters. The volume of data between these two points is large enough to justify a direct private-line arrangement. In the Eastern division, on the other hand, the sales offices, the factory and the headquarters are connected on a party-line arrange-

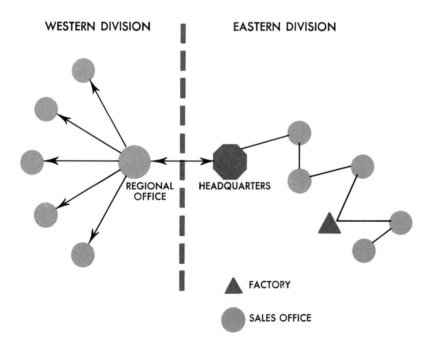

Figure 16. A communications network for a typical two-division company. This network utilizes a "one-to-many," a "one-to-one" and a "many-to-many" distribution pattern.

ment because of the considerable exchange of information between them. The distribution pattern in such a case is many-to-many.

A large flow of information from each of the Western division sales offices to the headquarters location in the East might have justified a direct link between each Western office and headquarters. In the existing situation, a relay through a collection point is adequate.

In the final analysis, the volume of information to be transmitted between the various points determines the most feasible communication service.

**Volume of the Information.** After the flow of information within a company has been established, the next step in determining the needs of the communication system is to calculate the volume of information to be handled at each location. The most common measure of volume per location is the total number of characters handled. Frequently, the number of characters is converted to "bits,"[1] a more precise measure obtained by multiplying the number of characters by a factor associated with the code to be used in the transmission of the data.[2] However, for most purposes, it is not necessary to carry volume calculations beyond total number of characters.

Calculation of the average daily volume and the peak volume of information to be handled in the system consists of four steps:

1. Calculate the average daily volume of messages presently flowing in the system.
2. Calculate the average number of characters in each message.
3. Calculate the average daily total transmission time.
4. Calculate the peak volumes.

The communications designer must plan the system to handle the peak traffic loads with acceptable delay as well as the total traffic load.

For simplicity, discussion will generally assume a two-point system with data flowing in only one direction. As more points are added to the system the calculation would remain the same but would be repeated for the data sent and received at each location.

*Calculate Call Volume.* The first step in calculating the volume of information that must be handled by the data communications system is to determine the number of messages (called "traffic") handled in an average day. This is done for traffic to and from

---

[1] See glossary for definition.
[2] Every code and some transmission systems have their own peculiar number of bits per character. The ASCII Code, for example, uses seven bits to identify each character. (See Figure 38, P. 124.)

every point in the system. The volume is calculated by taking a sample of several days' traffic and actually counting the number of messages handled each day at each location. The number of days to be included in the study is based upon the estimated number of messages that are handled in a month. An estimate of the monthly volume should be made, and the following table may be used as a guide in determining the number of days to be studied.

| Estimated Monthly Message Volume | Number of Days to Be Studied |
|---|---|
| Under 1000 | 20 |
| 1000 to 2000 | 10 |
| 2000 to 5000 | 5 |
| 5000 to 10,000 | 3 |
| 10,000 and over | 2 |

Ideally the working days to be studied should be chosen at random, but if for any reason a series of consecutive days must be selected, care should be taken to avoid days immediately preceding or following holidays. In addition, the count must be made at each location from which information is sent and at which information is received.

*Calculate the Characters Per Message.* The second step in calculating the volume of information is to select a random sample of messages presently being sent within the company, from which the average number of characters per message will be determined. The sample, of course, should be selected by standard statistical methods. The desirable size of the sample depends upon the required degree of accuracy. For example, assuming a normal distribution of message lengths, the probability is 98% that the following sample sizes will determine the average message length within the limits of accuracy shown on the right.

| Number of Messages in Sample | Probable Maximum Percent of Error |
|---|---|
| 100 | ± 12% |
| 200 | ± 8% |
| 500 | ± 5% |
| 1,000 | ± 4% |

In other words, if the average message length in a sample of 500 messages chosen from a company's traffic is found to be 323 characters, there is a 98% probability that the average length of all the company's messages is within 323 ± 5%, or somewhere between 307 and 339 characters.

After the sample messages have been selected, five items of information about each message should be recorded:

1. Point of origin
2. Destination
3. Length
4. Filing time (the time the originator *wanted* to send the message)
5. Charges

Four of these items are self-explanatory, but the method of calculating the length of the message should be discussed in more detail.

*Figure 17* represents a typical sales order that might be issued

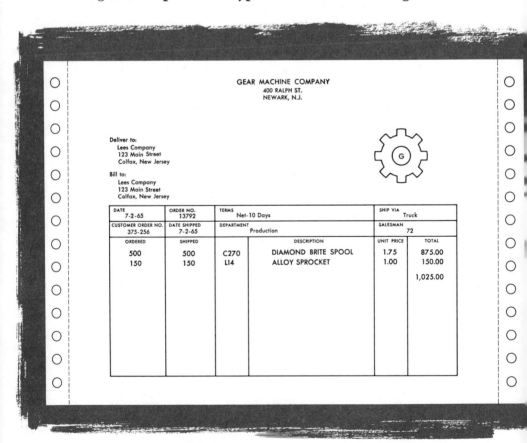

Figure 17. A typical sales order form.

from an outlying sales office to headquarters or a factory.

The order might be typed on a teleprinter and the information simultaneously sent over a communication line to a distant machine. The sales order constitutes one message if it is the only transmission on a call placed from the sales office to the headquarters or factory. If, on the other hand, it is grouped on a call with one or more other orders, the entire transmission is a single message.

For purposes of this explanation, it will be assumed that the sales order is one complete message. The only requirement, therefore, is to count the number of characters on the order—no averaging is involved. It should be borne in mind that every machine operation requiring a transmission signal must be counted as a character. Thus the analyst must count not only visible printed characters, but also word spaces, carriage return (the movement of the typing unit back to the left-hand margin), and line feed (the movement of the paper to position the typing unit at the next line). Each of these control functions can take place only if a signal is sent on the line to the receiving machine.

Additional characters must be accounted for when the receiving machine performs a time-consuming operation such as moving the carriage all the way across the page. Buffer (non-printing and non-controlling) characters must be included after the character that initiates the mechanical action to avoid the possibility that the first character on the next line will be transmitted while the carriage is in motion returning to the left margin and be printed in error part-way across the page. All such special characters must be counted in the message length, as they consume transmission time.

The need to count control characters points up the importance of efficient form design. Every item of information should be placed on the form so as to avoid waste of time in moving from one location to the next. *Figure 18* is an example of a form that was designed with this feature in mind. Without sacrificing legibility, every piece of information has been carefully placed on the form to avoid unnecessary movement from one item to the next. "Horizontal tabulation" permits the carriage of the teleprinter to skip rapidly over a number of spaces to a pre-set position. This would also ensure that information is properly spaced or lined up with a column of figures. Another action, called "vertical tabulation," moves the paper vertically to position the typing unit at a pre-set line on the form. A third such feature, "form-out" (or "form-feed"), allows the rapid feed-out of one form and the alignment of the next at the correct line to commence typing. These special controls provide a great advantage but require more expensive terminal equipment.

If the message to be examined is in paper tape form, it is possible to determine the number of characters by multiplying the length of the tape in inches by the number of characters per inch. Teleprinter tape, for example, has ten characters to the inch. Since all the control and buffer characters are already punched in the tape, they are counted at the same time. If each message is twenty inches long, for example, the number of characters in the message is 20 (inches) X 10 (characters per inch), or 200.

If a great deal of tape has to be measured, it is more practical to read the tape through a tape reader that operates at a fixed rate and then simply multiply the length of time necessary to read the tape by the operating rate of the reader. The tape reader on some teleprinters reads at a fixed rate of ten characters per second. If the time required to read a message tape is 125 seconds, the number of characters in the message is 10 (characters per second) X 125 (seconds), or 1250.

Punched cards are also easily checked for the number of characters. One has only to know how many cards are sent in one

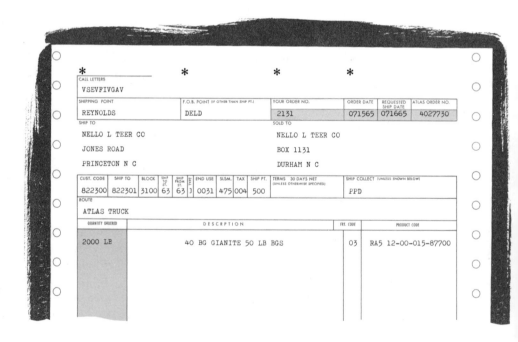

Figure 18. Teleprinter transmission time can be reduced if the form is designed to reduce the movement of the typing unit from one item on the form to the next. The asterisks identify the pre-set locations where horizonal tabulation would stop the form for typing.

transmission and how many characters are punched in each card. Care must be taken, however, to consider the type of card reader being used, for some readers will read every card column, whether or not there is a character in that column, while others can rapidly "skip-out" over the rest of the card after reading the last character.

*Calculate the Total Transmission Time.* The third step, after calculating the average number of characters per message, is to determine the average daily total transmission time. At this point a transmission speed must be assumed. This transmission time can be calculated by dividing the average number of characters per message by the assumed speed of the system. If the average message has 2,500 characters, for example, and the assumed transmission speed is 10 characters per second, the average transmission time per message will be 250 seconds. To this figure, however, must be added some operating time for dialing the call, waiting for the connection to be established and, in some cases, coordinating the forthcoming transaction with the personnel at the receiving end. Operating time should be calculated from a study of a sample of calls, but if this is impracticable, the system designer may use 100 seconds as an overall average for the operating time on each dialed-up data communications call.

After the average holding time (message time plus operating time) per message has been determined, the average daily total transmission time at each location can be calculated by multiplying the holding time by the average number of messages per day.

*Calculate the Peak Volume.* The fourth step is to determine the peak volume of information that a communication system must handle. In most systems, calls are not evenly distributed throughout the day but tend to build up during the middle of the morning and again, to a lesser extent, during the middle of the afternoon. To arrive at an accurate figure the actual variation in calling volume during the day should be studied. If this step is not possible, some approximations, derived from a host of studies, may be substituted. During an average eight-hour work day, for example, approximately 17% of the calls occur during the "busy hour." The corresponding figure in a 12-hour day is 14%; and in a 24-hour day, 12%. As these are average figures, they should, of course, be used with discretion.[3]

These busy-hour figures should also be adjusted to reflect seasonal fluctuations and possible growth.

---

[3] In some systems, the calls are not generated at random, and busy-hour calculations may not be necessary. For example, in an operation where all calls originate from a central location on a prearranged schedule, the number of calls during any specific hour can be planned ahead and thus be determined with a great deal of accuracy.

Another factor to consider in calculating total transmission time is the relation of assumed transmission speed to the capacity of the system. If, after completing the calculations, the total transmission time appears too great for the system to handle, it may be necessary to use a higher transmission speed or perhaps add more circuits to the system.

*Figure 19* is a summary of the various calculations used to determine the busy-hour traffic load flowing in one direction between two points. These busy-hour calculations are then used to determine the network configuration and the number of circuits required.

Figure 19.

## CALCULATION OF BUSY HOUR TRAFFIC
## FLOWING IN ONE DIRECTION BETWEEN TWO POINTS

| | |
|---|---|
| Average number of characters per message (Including spaces, control and buffer characters) | 4300 Characters / message |
| Transmission speed (Assuming 10 characters / second) | ÷ 10 Characters / second |
| Average transmission time / message | 430 Seconds / message |
| Average operating time | + 100 Seconds / message |
| Average total holding time | 530 Seconds / message |
| Average number of messages / day | X 30 Messages / day |
| Average daily transmission time | 15,900 Seconds / day or 265 Minutes / day |
| Busy hour load (assume an 8 hr. / day operation) | X 17% |
| System usage in busiest hour | 45.05 Minutes |

**Urgency of Information.** When rapid response is important, the system designer must consider all factors that can create delays. A system, for example, which incorporates many locations calling into one location on a random basis, may have too many calls arriving at that one point at the same time. In all probability, several of the callers would receive busy signals. This can be a problem when the delayed information is urgent. Even if the data is not urgent, the incomplete calls are a waste of time for the personnel who must engage in repeated efforts to forward their information. The same problem occurs when many messages are waiting to be sent over a single line.

The amount of delay to be expected during the busy hour depends upon the holding time of the circuit at the receiving location and the total number of minutes in the busy hour during which information will be received. Data communication planners refer to a series of charts which indicate the expected delay in transmissions when holding time, circuit use, and number of circuits in the group are known factors. The number of incoming circuits affects the probability that a calling part will receive a busy signal.

A full-duplex circuit provides more rapid exchange of two-way traffic between two points. With this type of circuit, information can be transmitted in both directions at the same time, substantially reducing the total holding time for the flow of information in both directions. Such an operation should be considered where outlying offices call in periodically during the day to submit sales or other type information. While the outlying office is forwarding its information, the headquarters location could simultaneously send back administrative messages.

The urgency of the information is an important factor in selection of the transmission medium to be used. For example, comparing facsimile and magnetic tape transmission, an 8½" × 11" sheet of paper (about 250 words of doubled-spaced copy) takes about six minutes to send by facsimile over a channel used for regular telephone calls. With the same type of channel in the same period of time, however, a magnetic tape transmitter can send about 15,000 words. Of course, rate of speed in the case of facsimile transmission varies with the size of the printing on the sheet, but the illustration points up the problem created by the speed difference. But, as will be seen later, the objectives of the system may make facsimile transmission ideal.

While in most systems, the required urgency is not the controlling factor in the basic design of a communications system, it does influence the ultimate decision regarding the number of circuits and the speed of transmission to be used.

Generally speaking, the controlling factor in determining the transmission speed to use in the system is the volume of information to be handled rather than the speed with which each message must travel from place to place. There is little practical difference in most cases in the time for a single message to travel from one point to another using different speeds. If a 10-character-per-second system is used, a 50-character message will arrive at its destination in five seconds. With a 300-per-character-per-second system, the same message will arrive in one sixth of a second. For occasional messages, the small saving in time is rarely worth the cost of the higher-speed system. However, if many messages must be handled by the system, requiring a total transmission time for the slower system of 12 hours per day, the higher-speed system would handle the same volume in 24 minutes.

**Language of the Information.** The term "language" is used in relation to information in two ways. First, it can be used to describe the *physical* form or medium of the information. This physical form may be "hard" copy (i.e., handwritten or printed pages), magnetic tape, punched cards, punched paper tape, imprinted magnetic ink characters, microfilm, cathode ray tube visual display,[4] or even the electrical internal memory elements of a computer such as magnetic cores. The appropriate information medium at the sending end may not satisfy requirements at the receiving end. To illustrate, an application for a loan on a life insurance policy may first appear in handwritten form, whereas the data processing center may want that information in punched-card form. If the information is to be transmitted over a data communication system, the handwritten form must either be converted to machine language at the transmitting terminal or transmitted by facsimile. If the main office must have the applicant's signature on file, facsimile transmission would be essential.

The second way in which the term "language" is applied to information has to do with the code used to record the information. Codes for recording information vary in relation to both the number of code elements (also called levels or bits) used to define a character and the assignment of the characters to each particular code combination. Current codes use anywhere from four to twelve code elements (or bits) to define each character.

In use today are over sixty different codes to transfer information. Most of these codes were devised for computers and other business

---

[4] Visual display devices are discussed in the Supplementary Information Section.

machines. However, five are commonly used for communications:

1. 5-level code used for most teleprinter systems today[5] ("Baudot" Code)
2. 6-level BCD (Binary Coded Decimal) type code
3. 6-level Teletypesetter code
4. 7-level Field Data code
5. 7-level ASCII code (American Standard Code For Information Interchange) (*Figure 38, page 124*)

Each of the first four listed codes has a number of variations. With the 5-level teleprinter code, for instance, there are four variations in use in the United States and one other in Europe. The variations do not occur in the alphabetic or numeric character assignments but rather in the characters which are assigned as special symbols or for control purposes. Of the above, the ASCII is the only code that is an American standard.

When designing an information system, it is necessary to consider the different forms and codes of information that may be needed. As a rule, when information appears in different media (e.g., punched cards and punched paper tape), the information will also be in a different code. The system must be designed for compatibility of all its various components. The system must be able to accept all the information in the form in which it occurs and deliver it in the form in which it is required.

For example, all of the following might be accomplished in connection with a sales order:

1. Preparation, by means of a teleprinter keyboard, of a page copy and a punched paper tape from the original handwritten order.
2. Transmission of the paper tape to the computer center where it is read into the computer.
3. The computer's conversion of the transaction into its own internal language.
4. As a result of processing the order, production by the computer of the following information.
   —Shipping papers which are sent to the proper warehouse for the order to be picked and shipped.
   —Billing instructions stored on an output magnetic tape until a shipping notice has been received.
   —An appropriate change in the inventory status and sales statistics records in the computer's random access memory.

---

[5] Those four-row keyboard teleprinters having an expanded character set use one of the other codes because they require more than 5 bits for the larger number of characters.

5. Upon receipt of an inquiry for stock status or sales statistics, presentation of the desired information at the inquirer's remote cathode ray tube visual display device.

Since it is usually not possible to have information in the same language (either code or physical form) throughout the information system, some language conversion becomes necessary. For example, the original form of the data may have to be changed or it may be necessary to provide clerical help to convert the data to a form suitable for transmission. It is considered good practice to capture original data in machine-sensible language at the source if possible. Any further language transformation required can then be handled by machine with less chance for human error and generally at lower costs.

One of the ways to handle conversion at the sending location is to have key-punch operators transcribe the information from handwritten sales to a deck of punched cards. On the other hand, a teleprinter operator might type the order and prepare a punched paper tape at the same time. It is also possible for conversion to be completed at the receiving end. Sales orders can be remitted to the headquarters by facsimile so that cards can be key-punched at the data processing center. Another technique is preparation and transmission of punched-paper tape at an outlying sales office, while at the receiving end, where punched cards are needed, a converter is used to receive the coded paper tape signals and convert them to the code of a card punch. *(Figure 20.)* The resultant punched cards will contain all the information that was in the punched paper tape. An important part of the designer's task is to ensure that the form of the original data allows it to be used as is or to be readily converted.

The process of conversion usually adds both time and cost to the operation of the system. In the example above, where incoming signals were converted from the code of the paper tape to the code of the punched cards, the cost of the converter was added to the system. If the converter had not been connected directly to the line but had been used to convert the received paper tape to cards, additional time would have been required to complete this separate operation. The factors of extra time and cost must be carefully considered in designing an information system that incorporates a conversion process.

**Accuracy of the Information.** Strictly speaking, errors in the communications system occur only in two areas: the terminal equipment itself and the transmission line. But it would be misleading

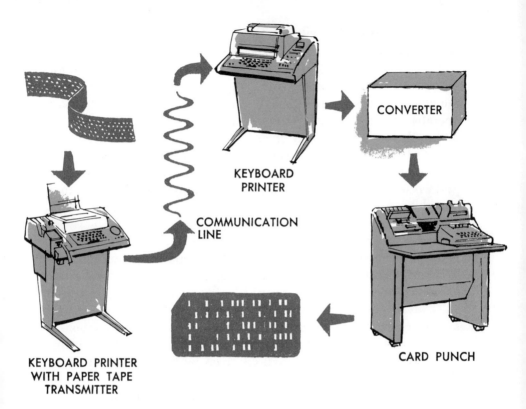

CONVERTER

KEYBOARD
PRINTER

COMMUNICATION
LINE

KEYBOARD PRINTER
WITH PAPER TAPE
TRANSMITTER

CARD PUNCH

Figure 20. A system for transmitting punched paper tape and receiving the data in punched card form.

to discuss error performance without consideration of human errors in the preparation of the data, which usually account for the largest portion of the total errors in a system.

In a study of its own typing pool, the Bell Telephone Laboratories discovered that the overall incidence of error among its typists was one mistake for every 1,000 characters typed (i.e., keystrokes). Errors that the typist caught immediately were not counted. The study was based on retyping of material already in typewritten form, so it can be expected that the incidence of error when typing from handwritten material will be somewhat higher.

Another study,[6] reported in the *Journal of Applied Psychology*, indicated that in keypunching the error rate average ranged from one in every 1,600 to one in every 4,300 keystrokes. Again, any errors that were detected immediately by the keypunch operator were not counted.

[6] E. T. Hemmer and G. R. Lockhead, "Productivity and Errors in Two Keying Tasks: A Field Study," **Journal of Applied Psychology** (1962), Vol. 46, No. 6, pp. 401-408.

In both cases, it has been estimated by some authorities, the use of verification would have reduced the error rate by 90-99%.

No data is available as to the incidence of error in data transmission terminal equipment such as paper tape or card readers and punches. In general, however, terminal equipment in good repair operates virtually without error. If a fault does occur the machine will probably commit many errors until it is repaired. This kind of trouble is much easier to locate than infrequent intermittent errors.

A number of studies have been conducted to determine the error performance of telephone lines.[7] On telephone lines like those that would be used for data transmitted over conventional dialed-up telephone service, approximately 70% of the calls would have an error rate of about one character for every 10,000 transmitted. This figure assumes no automatic error detection and correction (EDC). With error detection and correction equipment this rate would decrease to about one error for every 10 million characters transmitted.

These figures indicate that the first area for a program of improving error performance is in the preparation of the data by humans. This is not to say that the other two areas should be ignored, but more accuracy will ultimately be derived by first concentrating on the preparation area.

In determining whether or not to adopt an EDC system, the costliness and consequences of any error must be weighed against the cost of installing the error detection system. For example, in a simple telegram or teleprinter message, in which all the information appears in word form, an error in one or two letters usually does not prevent a reader from understanding the message. With training, the human mind can become an effective error detection and correction system; it can readily identify the letter in error and make corrections. Of course, the more unrelated the content of the message, the more difficult it is to detect a random mistake. In a list of unrelated numbers, for example, it is almost impossible to tell if one is incorrect.

Consider the situation in America's space program where a man has been placed in orbit around the earth. An error here could result in loss of life. During a space shot, telemetry data is processed not only at the launching site but also at remote computers. Every effort is made to be sure that the data is transmitted and received accurately. Cost is certainly considered, but the prime consideration

[7] R. L. Townsend and R. N. Watts, "Effectiveness of Error Control in Data Communications Over the Switched Telephone Network," The Bell System Technical Journal (November, 1964), Vol. 43, No. 6, p. 2611.

A. A. Alexander, R. M. Gryb and D. W. Nast, "Capabilities of the Telephone Network for Data Transmission," The Bell System Technical Journal (May, 1960), Vol. 39, p. 431.

is the accuracy of the data and its effect on the life of the astronaut. In a system containing only word messages for human use, therefore, it is usually not practical to include expensive error detection and correction devices. The chance of an error causing a great deal of trouble is small while the equipment to prevent the error is expensive.

Somewhere between the two extremes lies the bulk of most business "accuracy" problems. Technical ability to provide almost complete accuracy is available, but cost is usually the controlling factor.

## Design Alternative
## Data Communications Systems

After the factual data concerning the information to be handled in the system has been collected and analyzed, the next step is to design several alternative systems. Experience plays an important part in this area. Early in his review of the information flow an experienced analyst will begin to formulate ideas about how the final system should be designed. On the basis of his past experience, he will automatically reject some possibilities and will relate his current analysis to previous information systems he has designed.

While this approach may seem to have many advantages, there are some pitfalls to be avoided. Once an analyst has developed a preconceived notion of what the system might ultimately accomplish, his subsequent analysis of the problem may lose some of its objectivity. The danger always exists that he will tend to overlook details in the analysis that do not support the opinion he has already developed.

After the factors described in this chapter have been analyzed, the systems analyst should prepare a number of conceptual drawings showing different data communication configurations that meet the required specifications of the system. The drawings should show the various points on the system, the communication links between them, and the form of the information at various points. At this stage the equipment may be shown simply as boxes, with the functions they are to perform clearly indicated. *Figure 21* shows how a diagram of this type might look. It describes a system in which sales orders are typed in branch sales offices on equipment that simultaneously prepares a punched-paper tape. These tapes are then transmitted to the main office where punched cards are prepared for input to the centralized data processing system.

Using these various conceptual drawings the analyst can begin to apply the statistics developed from his study of the volume, urgency, and accuracy requirements of the system. He determines such factors as:

1. The speed of transmission.
2. The type of communication service that should be used.
3. The number of communication circuits required.
4. The desirability of some form of code over another.
5. The advisability of "on-line" or "off-line" conversion.
6. The amount of floor space required for the equipment at all locations.

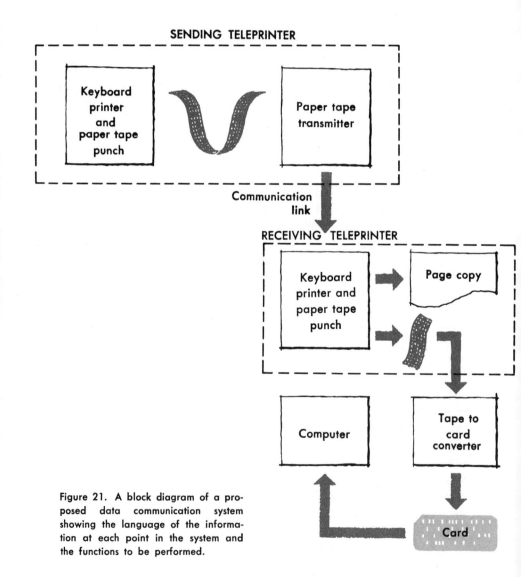

Figure 21. A block diagram of a proposed data communication system showing the language of the information at each point in the system and the functions to be performed.

At first, the system designer should consider "ideal" systems without regard to the availability of existing hardware or communications services. If some of the desirable equipment is not available, consideration should be given to developing it. If such development does not appear justifiable, he must consider compromises in equipment or system design.

The various system designs that may solve the problem may be quite similar. The various designs may include teleprinters, card readers, and magnetic tape equipment using a variety of communication services.

The Custer Oil Company case at the end of this text is an example of how three different data communications systems can all solve the same problem. A designer of data communication systems must be familiar with all of the many services and equipment available from the communications companies as well as with the many different types of terminal equipment available from the manufacturers of business equipment.

## Determine the Costs
## of Each Alternative System

After the alternative systems have been designed, it is necessary to determine how much each system will cost. If the system is to be leased, the cost is usually not difficult to determine, since equipment and communication channels are usually charged for on a per-month basis. If the system is to be largely owned, the problem becomes more complicated because such things as capital recovery and rate of return must also be considered.

In considering a system, there are five primary kinds of costs that must be evaluated. In addition to the two main costs of equipment and communication channels mentioned above, there will also be:

Personnel expense—the salaries of those employees who will operate the system. This expense should include the "loaded cost" of the employee, not just the salary. This loaded cost will include such things as social security tax, pension funds, hospitalization expenses, etc. This personnel expense should be considered even if an employee devotes only a few hours a day to the operation of the system. The cost of that employee should be reduced to an hourly figure and included in the cost of operating the system.

Expenses for supplies – the printed forms, paper tape, punched cards, printing ribbons, etc.

Expenses charged for the use of floor space — the charges to cover rent, building maintenance, light, heat, etc.

These various costs should be reduced to some common denominator so that they may be added together and compared in relation to different systems. This common denominator can be based on any period of time but many analysts find that a monthly figure is the most useful. Usually for leased systems the equipment and communications costs are already stated in terms of a monthly expense. The personnel expense can easily be converted to a monthly figure. If some regular or periodic overtime is involved, some average figure can be included in the monthly total. The expenses for supplies and floor space can also be reduced to monthly figures without much trouble.

### Evaluate the Alternative Systems

After the various systems have been designed and the cost of each determined, it is necessary to evaluate each system and determine which one will best satisfy the requirements of the problem. This evaluation process usually takes place on a continuing basis as the system is being designed. Consequently, clearly unsuitable systems can be dropped before they have been completely designed.

In the event that several possible systems are completely designed, the following formal evaluation technique will help to determine which system provides the best overall solution. The evaluation is broken down into four basic questions.

**How Well Does Each System Meet the Objectives?** The proposed system must completely satisfy the objectives as they were defined for the study. When it is finally implemented, the system may be more comprehensive than the requirements of the original problem, but it may not be less.

The objective of a new system as it was originally defined, for example, may have been to bring sales data to the data processing center. The systems being evaluated might all meet this objective but in several different ways. One system might bring the data in every four hours, another within an hour of the close of business, and still another by midnight of that day. All these systems meet the basic objective, but to different degrees.

The system which brings the data in every four hours may seem to be good, but if it is later decided that the data will be processed only once each day, data arriving in the middle of the day must be held until the appointed processing time. The second system provides the data by approximately six o'clock in the evening, in time for an evening run in the data processing center. The third system also gets the data into the center the same day, but too late for processing that evening. Here, then, are three systems, all of which meet the basic objective but one of which is obviously better than the others.

This illustration also points out the need for well-defined objectives. The objective as it was stated above was quite general: "bring sales data to the data processing center." This type of general objective made it possible for several systems to meet it and an evaluation was necessary to select the best system. If the objective had been stated more specifically as: "bring the sales data to the data processing center in time for an 8 P.M. data processing run," the choice would automatically have been reduced to either of the first two systems.

The first step, then, in an evaluation of a data communication system is to see how well each system meets the objectives that were set forth for the solution of the problem.

**How Well Does Each System Meet the Specifications?** Earlier in the study, after the objective of the system had been defined, the facts about the information flowing in the system were analyzed. From this analysis came a set of specifications concerning the distribution, volume, urgency, language and accuracy of the communication system. Of course, each system must meet the specifications as a group, but there may be a "give and take" between the various factors. For example, even though there may be a requirement for punched cards at both the sending and receiving stations, in the interest of faster transmission speeds it may be necessary to convert the punched cards to punched paper tape for transmission and then convert back again to punched cards at the receiving location. This conversion may be more economical than using a higher speed punched card transmission system to gain the speed advantage. This example illustrates a compromise that may be suggested by the differing requirements of language, urgency and cost.

Each of the five factors will have to be evaluated individually and also as a group. Compromises will have to be evaluated in terms of their overall effect on the system operation.

**How Much Does Each System Cost?** The third area of evaluation is the cost of each of the systems under consideration. The direct costs can usually be determined by using the procedure outlined earlier, but these costs must be evaluated in relation to the benefits that each system provides. Two systems, for example, may solve an information problem as it was originally defined. System A may cost $1,000 per month and System B may cost $2,000 per month. On a simple comparison basis, System A would be the better one to choose. However, if System B provides benefits that would result in additional savings or gains of $1,500 per month, it would become the better system. Even though it costs $1,000 per month more than System A, System B also solves the basic problem and at a net cost of only $500 per month.

This cost evaluation, then, only starts with listing the direct costs of each system. These costs must then be related to the benefits provided.

**What Other Benefits Does Each System Provide?** In designing a data communication system to solve a particular problem, the first benefit to be expected is the solution of the problem. This anticipated benefit may be expressed in either tangible or intangible form. It may be to reduce costs, improve customer service, or help the company in many other ways.

However, during the process of evaluation, additional benefits provided by some of the suggested systems may become apparent. These added benefits may also be either tangible or intangible. The tangible benefits are those to which actual dollar amounts can be assigned, usually in the form of savings over the old method of operation. These savings will generally occur in the following areas:

Equipment — Frequently some equipment that was used in the old system will be eliminated. Its operating expense, rental, and, if owned, depreciation, maintenance, and property taxes will all constitute direct savings that can be credited to the new system.

Personnel — Frequently less employee time will be required to operate under the new system. Even a reduction of only a few hours' time for several people should be counted as a savings. As in computing costs of the new system, the loaded employee cost should be used in determining any savings the new system will provide.

Cost of Capital — If the new system permits a company to decrease the size of its inventories or shortens the length of the billing cycle, the amount of money that must be invested in the business is reduced. The long term capital invested in the business stems from equity funds plus borrowings. The cost of equity capital is based on the economic principle of "opportunity costs", i.e., what the money could earn if invested elsewhere in the business. Borrowed funds bear a direct interest cost. Any reduction in cash requirements, therefore, represents an indirect and a direct saving to the company.

Other Savings — Under this category could be included such savings as reduction in floor space for the new system, the elimination of some operation locations such as branch offices, the reduced cost of record storage, a reduction in supplies such as punched cards, and an elimination of mailing expense.

In addition to the tangible benefits there may also be some other gains in the form of intangible benefits that the new system will provide. These may include improved service to the customers, faster receipt of sales information or improved coordination between departments. Even though it is difficult to place a dollar value upon such benefits, a manager may very well decide that the ability of one system to provide these intangible benefits justifies a slightly higher cost. His decision will be based not on a slide rule calculation but on his experience as a manager.

It is important that all benefits, both tangible and intangible, be considered in the evaluation of the potential systems. This is the point at which the decision must be made as to which system provides the best overall solution to the problem.

## Implement
## the Selected System

The final installation of any system is usually the most rewarding experience of the entire project. For the first time the designer will see the equipment working and the information flowing in the desired manner. However, this stage can prove frustrating if prior planning and training are inadequate and difficulties arise in getting the new system started.

The employees who are to work with the new system should be thoroughly trained, and they should be given time to practice operating the system in order to become familiar with its various aspects. The more practice the operators have, the less problems there will be when the system is cut over into actual operation. Some companies, on the basis of their own experience, now recommend that employees who will be actively engaged in operating any new system be included in the consultations prior to the final planning and implementation stage. When the operators themselves participate in the planning process, they usually take a more personal interest in the success of the system.

Another possible source of trouble stems from the fact that some systems do not function perfectly when they are first cut into service.

There will frequently be "bugs" here and there that must be eliminated. Before making any decision regarding major changes, management must allow enough time for the system to overcome any initial problems and perform as intended.

If the new system is to occupy an important place in a larger information system, early dependability of operation is a real necessity. In such instances some type of emergency temporary back-up system should be arranged. During the early testing period, this back-up system could be the old operation if it can be preserved intact for a short time.

If the overall system is to be large, a gradual phasing-in of the new system should be considered. In cases where many locations are to be included, for example, it might be desirable to engage in a step-by-step conversion. This gradual conversion is advantageous, for it permits deficiencies to be uncovered before installation of the entire system is completed. It also allows the equipment suppliers to spread their deliveries over a period of time.

### Follow-up

**Make Sure That the System Meets the Objectives.** Although a system design may look ideal on paper, the real test of its suitability will come during its actual operation. The operating system should be carefully studied to see that it actually does solve the problem, satisfy the objectives, and meet the specifications.

**Determine Changing Requirements.** Since most companies are always in a state of change, no system can be designed to last forever. Companies will add, eliminate and change locations; they will grow larger or smaller; their product lines and methods of operation will change. All these changes will in turn require other changes in the methods of handling information. The data communications system will have to be modified from time to time to fit these changes.

After the communication system has been installed, there should be a periodic review of the system to determine when changes should be made. Included in this review should be all the communications of a company because some change in the company's voice communication needs may have a significant effect upon the existing data communication system. For example, the voice traffic between two points in the company may have grown so much that a private line can be justified. This line could then also be used for data communications.

In a re-evaluation of an existing data communication system, the same seven steps described in this chapter should be followed. If no significant changes have been uncovered after completing Step 2 (the collection of facts about the flow of information in the system) and there is no substantial increase in voice requirements, it can be assumed that the system is still satisfactory and no changes are needed unless, however, new equipment, communication services or techniques have made the old system obsolete.

**Summary**

The summary of steps involved in planning a data communication system is shown in *Figure 22*. It is first necessary to define the

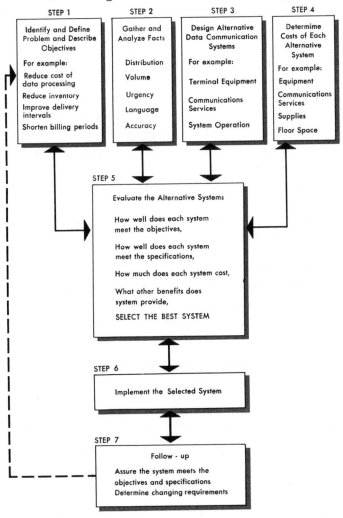

Figure 22. A Summary of the steps involved in planning a data communications system.

problem to be solved and the objectives of a new communication system. Second, the facts about the information flow must be collected and analyzed. These facts concern five different characteristics of the information: the distribution, the volume, the urgency, the language and the accuracy of the information. After analyzing these facts, the next step is to design several different data communication systems that will satisfy the requirements of the information flow. The fourth step is to determine the cost of each of these systems. Fifth, compare the various systems to see which one best satisfies the requirements and gives the most benefits for the cost.

The next step is to implement the solution to the problem by installing the system. And finally, continuous follow-up is necessary to ensure that the system continues to satisfy the changing information needs of the company.

A study of a company's communication problems should involve more than just the movement of information flowing within the company. It may develop into a study of the entire data processing needs of the business; or it may bring up questions about such things as where the information originates, where the information is needed, what kind of information is needed, and how the information is used in the operation of the business. This type of study will certainly involve both data processing and data communications.

In any examination of the overall information needs of a company, data communications should be considered early and continuously. If it is left to last it can be very difficult to design a system that fits all the company's requirements.

The techniques described in this chapter can best be learned by applying them to realistic business situations. At the end of this text are three cases that can be used for this purpose.

### Discussion Questions

1. Discuss each of the five characteristics of information that must be considered in designing a data communication system.
2. What problems are created by the existence of many different codes?
3. Discuss the meaning of the statement: "the cost of correcting an error must not be more than the cost of ignoring the error."
4. Briefly describe how adding several new stations to an existing communication network will affect the five factors of design.
5. What are some of the intangible benefits which might be expected to result from an improved information system?

### Chapter VI

# TRENDS IN
# DATA
## COMMUNICATIONS

As the science of data communications comes of age, a number of trends and countertrends are affecting the pattern of its development. As in any new field of activity, forces and counterforces interact at an early stage and this interaction determines a course of growth in the new area. The multiplicity of these forces, to be sure, complicates the identification of the emerging trends.

### Computers and Data Communications

Most computers currently under design are compatible with communication channels. The obvious advantages of using communications to extend the capability of the computer has prompted computer manufacturers to produce both data processing computers with communication capabilities and communication switching computers with data processing capabilities. *(Figure 23.)*

The close bond between data processing and data communications will be further strengthened in the coming years. The two can be brought even closer together to create a more effective information system than either can produce on its own. The biologist calls this kind of relationship "symbiosis," i.e., the ability of two organisms to complement each other and live together to their mutual benefit.

### On-Line Real-Time Systems

Like data processing and data communications, on-line and real-time systems are so closely related that they also can be regarded as two sides of the same coin. There is, however, a conceptual difference between the two terms. *On-Line* means that all elements of the system, including any remote terminals, are interconnected with and under control of the computer. *Real-Time* is a term which describes the ability of an information system to collect data on

Figure 23. The General Electric Data Communications Processor: DATANET-30 is a computer designed to handle both message switching and on-line real-time data processing.

events as they occur, to process that data immediately, and to use the new information to influence succeeding events such as inquiries, transactions, special reports or manufacturing processes and operations.

Examples of on-line real-time information systems can be found among the reservation systems of many airlines. When a customer wishes to book a reservation on a flight, the ticket agent, using a special keyboard terminal which is on-line to the computer, questions the computer as to the availability of seats on that particular flight. The computer responds with the appropriate information. If a seat is available and the customer wishes to make a reservation, the agent then keys in an order for one seat. The computer immediately (*real-time*) records the reservation and changes the inventory of seats for that flight so that subsequent inquiries will reflect one less available seat.

This series of activities illustrate how an on-line real-time system accepts information about an event (the sale of a seat), processes it (makes the reservation and updates the inventory record), and uses the new information to influence succeeding inquiries (the next request finds one less available seat). A further extension of existing systems might have the computer programmed to keep track of requests for seats even when none are available and, when requests have reached a predetermined figure, initiate a report to schedule another aircraft for a particular flight.

In the coming years there will be an increase in the number of on-line real-time data transmission systems in use. Nevertheless, for the next five to ten years most systems will probably utilize batch processing and transmission techniques. Real-time systems are complex and expensive and may not be justified at this time for all information systems. The main area of application will be in transactions involving inventory and information files. These types of messages are usually short and require rapid response.

## Semi-Real Time

In semi-real time systems the data is collected at the source in real-time, i.e., when and where the event occurs, but the processing of the information about that event occurs at some later time, usually in a batch processing operation. The factory data collection system in *Figure 24* is a good example of a semi-real time operation.

In a typical production-line data collection system, workers report job progress to a central data collection point. The worker uses a special data transmission terminal to send in the information. This terminal will accept a punched card to identify the job being worked on, an employee card to identify the worker, and variable status information keyed in on pushbuttons or levers. This information is received at the data collection point and is punched into cards. The information is also checked for proper format and transmission errors. If either type of error occurs, the receiving terminal sends a signal back to the worker who must then send the information in again.

This data collection and modest amount of error checking occurs in real-time. If an error should occur, the information can be corrected and retransmitted while the event is still fresh in the worker's mind and before the data is entered into the processing operation. Errors found at the time of processing are not as easy to correct as they would have been at the time they were made. At the end of the day, or whenever the data is to be processed, the punched cards with the production information are assembled and processed in a batch operation. In this system, the modest amount of error control does keep many errors from entering the processing operation.

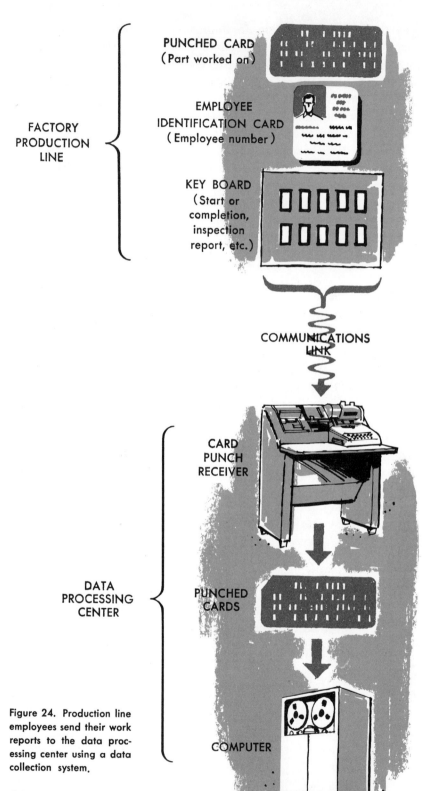

FACTORY PRODUCTION LINE

PUNCHED CARD
(Part worked on)

EMPLOYEE IDENTIFICATION CARD
(Employee number)

KEY BOARD
(Start or completion, inspection report, etc.)

COMMUNICATIONS LINK

DATA PROCESSING CENTER

CARD PUNCH RECEIVER

PUNCHED CARDS

COMPUTER

Figure 24. Production line employees send their work reports to the data processing center using a data collection system.

84

A second level of sophistication in the semi-real time operation is possible. Instead of an inexpensive data collection system with only a punched card output, a real-time computer could be used to collect the data. In a computer system the data would be checked not only for format and transmission errors, but also for reasonableness. A worker, for example, might have indicated that he spent 0050 (fifty) hours working on a project that should require only 0005 (five) hours. The difference could have been an unintentional error or a deliberate attempt to defraud the company. Both numbers would have satisfied the format check since each had four digits. The data, although it was incorrect, would have been entered into the processing cycle and the wages paid to this worker would have reflected the additional hours worked on the project.

If a computer is used to collect data, it can be programmed to check the reasonableness of a worker's spending 50 hours on that particular job. When the number appears to be outside the prescribed limits for that job, the system would indicate an error and the worker would have to re-enter the hours worked until the figure satisfies the reasonableness check. Of course, an overpayment resulting from an error like the one described here would probably have been caught by the payroll department. But in many systems the errors could result in more serious consequences, and a check on the reasonableness of the data before it is entered into the processing cycle could save a great deal of time and expense later.

The use of semi-real time systems will grow in popularity during the next several years. These systems provide many of the advantages of on-line systems without all the costly complexities of the real-time operation. One of the prime advantages of the semi-real time systems is that it is possible to maintain some control over the input data at a modest cost.

## Voice Communication in Computer Systems

One of the problems associated with the use of computers has been the necessity for translating information into a form which can be recognized by the computer. Systems planners look forward to the day when computers will be able to accept data in a form which is natural for people to use. Several new techniques are "breaking through" this technical barrier.

One of these techniques is the ability of a computer to "talk" with a person. The first version of this new technique permits a person to send a coded inquiry to a computer and in return receive a voice reply. The various words in the computer's vocabulary are prerecorded and, based on information in the computer, are used to reply to questions by selecting words in the proper sequence to form an answer to the question. This voice answerback capability of computers is fairly well developed and a number of companies are already using this new technique.

In a banking application, for example, tellers could call into a computer to request bank balance information on a particular account. The inquiry would be made on a special terminal device and would consist of an account number and a code identifying the desired information. The computer, after a search, would locate the account balance information and answer the question in audible words.

If the bank account were number 1234 with a balance of $14.54, for example, the computer would "say": "October eight account number one two three four balance one four point five four." The answer would be heard in a loudspeaker or in the receiver of a telephone associated with the inquiry terminal. In other applications, different words would be recorded in the memory. Since the words are recorded by a human voice, the computer can be equipped with any vocabulary and even speak in a Southern accent!

The ability of a computer to generate answers in audible words makes it possible to obtain a great deal of information in a form understood by anyone and with the use of unsophisticated and therefore inexpensive terminal equipment. A number of computer companies have designed inquiry devices. Telephones which use tones for dialing[1] can also be employed for this purpose by using the pushbutton tone dial after the call is established to submit the inquiry. In this case, the answer is heard in the telephone receiver.

Applications of voice answerback systems will be numerous. Brokers are installing this type of system to call a computer and inquire about the most recent trading price of a stock. A numeric stock code is entered along with the classification code of the desired information. The computer replies with the latest quote on the stock as well as the number of shares traded and any other pertinent information.

Retail stores, in an adaptation of this system, could call a centralized credit bureau and key in a customer's account number. In return, the computer could render a complete credit report on the customer. Hospitals could check on an incoming patient's hospitalization insurance status while admitting him. This service would be available from large centralized information bureaus set up for insurance purposes.

---

[1] Telephones of this type are described in detail in the Supplementary Information Section.

Voice answerback systems will increase in number as more computer manufacturers build the capability into their equipment. The increasing availability of tone dialing telephones will also hasten the use of these systems because the use of the regular telephone for inquiry and voice answerback permits almost anyone in any location to use the service.

The voice-in capability, i.e., the ability of the computer to hear and understand spoken words is still under development, and there are, of course, many problems associated with having the computer recognize words as they are spoken by different types of voices and in different accents. An experimental system makes use of a computer programmed to function as a travel agent. The computer asks the tourist certain relevant questions which can be answered either "yes" or "no." At this early stage of development, the computer can only understand these two words.

The computer may ask a question such as "do you enjoy golf?" If the response is "yes," the next query might then be "Do you like the mountains?" If the answer is "no" the subsequent question may be "Do you like the seashore?" Depending upon the "yes" or "no" answers to questions like these, the computer selects the next logical question and finally chooses a pre-selected vacation package for the customer based upon the entire range of responses. Simple as it may seem, a basic telephone serves as the inquiry device for this system. All that is required is the ability to talk to and listen to the computer.

### Terminal Equipment—
### Simplification of Operation

Since people are the final controlling link in an information system, planners are always seeking new ways to make terminal equipment easier to operate. Sometimes this effort produces terminal equipment which is quite expensive. Data collection terminals, for example, can become costly because they have the ability to accept data in many forms. Workers can enter data from punched cards, identification badges, pushbuttons, levers, and pre-set "data cartridges." These many forms are necessary to make it easy for workers to enter data as automatically as possible and thus reduce the possibility of errors. Airline ticket reservation terminals are also expensive because they are specially built to accept data quickly and easily and transmit it to the on-line computer.

One way to reduce the complexity of terminal equipment is to transfer some of its control functions to the computer. This has the advantage not only of reducing the complexity of the equipment but also of reducing its cost. Of course, this arrangement does make the computer installation more expensive but if many outlying stations are involved, the increase in cost at the computer will be more than offset by the reduction in cost at the outlying terminals.

One method of operation which uses the technique of allowing the computer to control the outlying stations is called the conversation mode of operation. With the conversation mode of operation, the terminal device receives all its instructions from the computer, and the operator has only to respond to its questions. The term is derived from the conversation type question-and-answer operation between computer and operator.

In most computer-based information systems, proper format of the data entered into the system is vital. Every piece of information must be entered in the proper sequence in relation to the other information in the transaction. Sometimes this rigid format requirement is too difficult to maintain when relatively unskilled operators enter data into the information system. To further complicate the situation, in many cases the operators do not work in the department responsible for the operation of the computer and computer personnel exercise no direct supervision over their activities.

In the future, a new human-computer conversation mode of operation will probably help simplify the problem of rigid formats. Operators will use simple teleprinter-like input devices which will be connected to the computer by means of communication channels. In lieu of complicated forms, the machines will use blank paper. After the operator has gone on-line to the computer, the computer will request each item of information.

For example, in a service order system now being studied by some telephone companies the first item the computer might request is the new customer's name. This question is typed by the computer in a color of ink different from the color used by the operator. After the telephone company's service-order writer has typed in the name the computer will then ask for the address by typing the question on the paper, again in the different-colored ink. As the service-order writer enters each requested item, the computer, in its turn, will automatically solicit a new piece of information. The operator need not even be concerned about the order in which the information is entered because the computer will automatically ask for the information in the proper order. The computer, in fact, will also print out from its memory all the information concerning existing telephone service in the house or apartment. *(Figure 25.)*

Although the use of the telephone as a data input device was discussed earlier, its full potiential was not emphasized. The tones

| | |
|---|---|
| NAME | JONES, JOHN |
| CREDIT INFORMATION | ENGINEER / EMERSON / 16 MO. |
| ADDRESS | 149 WALNUT ST. STL |
| EQUIPMENT LEFT IN SERVICE | 1 / 1FRGC / 1 / EXTBC |
| SERVICE AND EQUIPMENT | 1 / FREW / 1 / EXL / 1 / PRNLX1 / 1BEC |
| LOCAL SERVICE AMOUNT | $9.40 |
| PREVIOUS COLOR | * |
| NON-RECURRING CHARGES | $32.50 |
| DIRECTORY LISTING | * |
| TELEPHONE NUMBER | 555-2368 |
| CREDIT CLASS | C |
| DEPOSIT | $ |
| DUE DATE | 10-20 |
| REMARKS | CUSTOMER REQUESTS |
| | NOT WORK BEFORE 10 A.M. |

END

Figure 25. A sample telephone company service order prepared in a conversation mode. The questions and information typed by the computer are shown in color. The information typed by the service order writer is in black. The entries in the left hand column are printed out here for clarity but would normally be coded or abbreviated.

for dialing which are used by the pushbutton telephone are also available for transmitting information once the dialing has been completed and the call established. Eventually these telephones will be installed throughout the country as standard sets, and every telephone in the nation could then be used for the transmission of data. Because telephone service is easy to operate and is widely available, the telephone instrument itself becomes an ideal terminal device to gain access to computers. Someday a common user computer service may become available using the telephone as the input/output terminal.

The potential for some type of common user computer service was first discussed in 1961[2]. Professor John McCarthy of the Massachusetts Institute of Technology, in one of his lectures, introduced the notion of a computer utility[3] capable of supplying computer power to each customer where, when and in the amount needed. The method of operation of such a utility would be analogous to

---

[2] McCarthy, John, "Time-Sharing Computer Systems," in **Management and the Computer of the Future,** M. Greenberger, ed. Cambridge, Mass., The M.I.T. Press, 1962, pp 221-236.
[3] See glossary for further definition.

that of an electrical distribution system which supplies electrical power where and when required to facilitate the performance of physical work. In this case, the computer utility would supply logical power to aid an individual in solving his processing and computational problems. *(Figure 26.)*

To satisfy their special needs, the terminal equipment used by engineers and scientists would have to be relatively complex, but the terminal equipment used to serve individuals in their own homes would remain comparatively simple. In the latter case, perhaps the regular pushbutton telephone would suffice.

## Wider Variety of Terminal Equipment

Since data communications in its present form became available in the late 1950's, an increasing variety of terminal equipments have been designed and introduced for use with communications lines. This variety of terminal apparatus will almost certainly continue to increase in the coming years as additional applications for data

Figure 26. The computer center of the KEYDATA Corporation, one of the first companies to provide time-shared use of an on-line real-time computer to a wide variety of customers. The computer is a Digital Equipment Corporation PDP-6.

90

communications are developed. The next few pages will describe some of the newer developments in the area of terminal equipment.

**PICTUREPHONE Service.** PICTUREPHONE service is a recently developed service that permits the calling party to see as well as to hear the person with whom he is talking on the telephone. A long distance "booth-to-booth" service was established in 1964 on a trial basis between New York, Washington and Chicago. "See while you talk" calls were on an appointment basis. *(Figure 27.)*

While today only a head-and-shoulders image of a person is transmitted, the future holds many interesting possibilities. Someday it may be possible to transmit finely detailed printed material with clarity. Although a great deal of development work must be completed before this service is acceptable for any type of data transmission, its potential is evident.

**MICR Transmission.** MICR (Magnetic Ink Character Recognition) is a technique for electrically reading coded characters printed on documents (such as bank checks) in magnetic ink. Today, most bank checks are automatically sorted by machines that

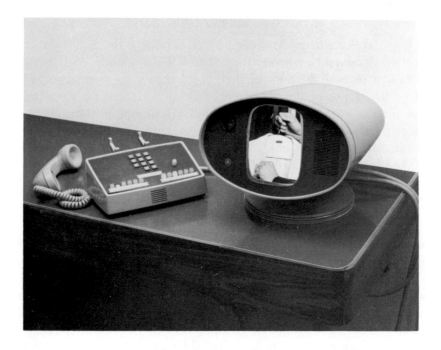

Figure 27. The experimental PICTUREPHONE service features a modern console with buttons to make calls and to control the video screen. In the future this new service may provide a means of data transmission.

recognize the MICR characters. As yet, however, machines are not able economically to read these characters and transmit the information directly over a communications line.

**High-Speed Facsimile.** The high-speed transmission of graphics is now practical with the use of wideband[4] communications service. Considerable work is also under way to enable the transmission of high-speed facsimile over regular voice-grade channels. Although a technological breakthrough is first required it is conceivable that documents and pictures will someday be transmitted over such channels in less than one minute per page.

**Remote Meter Reading.** One of the current challenges in the utility field is to develop a technique for automatically reading residential electric, gas and water meters. A number of systems have already been designed and special terminal equipment has been developed. The cost of the service, however, is not yet low enough to be generally competitive with manual reading.

**Microfilm Transmission.** A requirement has developed during the last few years for transmitting images that are recorded on microfilm records. Work has already progressed in this area, and a few terminals of this type are available today.

**Optical Scanning.** Another needed service is the facility to scan printed documents, convert the information to a code, and transmit it over a communications chanel. Techniques for optical scanning of certain types of documents have been perfected for some time, but for the required definition wideband communication channels must be used at present for transmission of the information in a reasonable length of time. Subsequent developments will probably make it possible to employ telephone channels for transmission.

### Communication Technology

Data communications owes its present state of development to advances in communication technology. Much work has been required to design data terminal equipment and new communication services which will permit the economical and reliable transmission of data over both dial-up telephone connections and private-line connections. While a great deal of research is under way in the field of communications in general, several new developments in particular are expected to have an effect upon data transmission.

Most obvious is the trend toward higher speeds over existing voice-grade channels. Transmission engineers have always aspired

---

[4] See glossary for definition.

to achieve higher speeds with existing circuits because of the flexibility and economics for data transmission inherent in utilization of the existing telephone network. New transmission techniques under development will permit data transmission over existing telephone channels at speeds up to 7,200 bits per second.

This trend toward higher line speeds will have an effect upon the design of terminal equipment. To take advantage of the higher speeds, new and different types of terminal equipment will have to be developed. At the present time the potential of high-speed terminal equipment is limited by the capacity of standard telephone lines.

In another area, the trend toward higher speeds will also affect the operation of some business information systems. With a higher rate of transmission, less circuit time per call will be required. When a large volume of information can be transmitted over a line in a very short length of time, the minimum time period for the call is frequently not fully used. In such instances users may find potential savings in storing and batching messages until enough data exists to fill the minimum calling time.

Another trend emphasizes the development of new types of communication channels. These channels not only will have the advantage of making higher speeds available, but also will reduce the cost of data communication channels. One system currently being developed will be capable of transmitting 220 million bits per second. This extremely high rate of transmission is more fully appreciated when one realizes that such a speed would make it possible to transmit the entire contents of Webster's New Collegiate Dictionary in less than *one second*. Of course, there are few users who would generate a volume of data sufficient to justify this speed. But there would also be benefits for smaller users. This new type channel would mean that more data messages could be carried on one channel with no increase in circuit cost. It would enable the communications common carriers to use their channels more efficiently for common user circuit arrangements.

Scientists view the millimeter wave guide as another interesting potential means of transmitting data and telephone conversations. The wave guide is a precision-built hollow tube capable of carrying a wide spectrum of radio waves. Its potential for data transmission is great, but the development of this type of transmission channel is still some years away.

A further step into the future, the laser, holds great promise for both voice and data transmission. The laser uses a beam of light to carry information. Although a great deal of work has already been done in this area, years of continued research remain before an economical laser-transmission system becomes a reality.

One of the most dramatic advances in communications, however, is now in operation. For the first time in history, satellite communication is providing a wide-band transmission path which is capable of transmitting data or television pictures to any point in the world. Until satellite communications were introduced, television pictures, which are a form of data, were recorded on film or, more recently, on magnetic tape and flown across the oceans to broadcasting stations. In addition to transmitting television, satellites can transmit data signals directly overseas at extremely high speeds.

### Conclusion

From the observations made here it is apparent that the field of data communications is undergoing rapid change. One of the communications common carriers began a three-month course in 1961 to train engineers, salesmen and operating managers in the design and application of data communication systems. This program has been in continuous operation since that time. By 1964, however, it was necessary to establish a second two-week course to update the early graduates of the school.

The trends in data communications that have been described here herald even greater changes in the future. Businessmen unfamiliar with the potential of data communications will not be prepared to take advantage of the new capabilities of computers and information systems. A McKinsey and Company study of 27 companies which have been working with computers for five years or more showed that variations in the way computers were used often caused million-dollar differences in net income between companies in the same industry.[5] The study predicted that those firms which continue to take advantage of even more advanced communication and data processing techniques will further increase their earnings advantage over those which do not.

The years ahead will see a growing complexity in data communications. No matter how large or fast or expensive computers become, scientists see no end to the need for more advance machines and more refined systems. Developing new computer techniques and programs to fill current needs often results in methods that lead to the quick solution of other related problems. The mathematics used to solve military logistics problems, for example, apply also to

---

[5] **Getting the Most Out of Your Computer.** A survey of company approaches and results. (McKinsey and Company, Inc., New York)

warehousing and distribution. As electronic data processing develops and improves, so also does data communications. The American way of life is destined to be noticeably affected by data communications. Its use will enable the computer to become a silent and remote partner in many routine activities ranging from voting in elections to banking from the home.

The individual may be affected in other ways. In the area of medical diagnosis, for example, continuous research and testing programs are now being conducted with data communications to transmit heartbeat and brain-wave recordings between the patient's bedside and the hospital. Data communications will be employed to control waiting time at traffic lights, to measure home consumption of fuel and electricity, to print student report cards, and to conduct computerized public opinion polls. As the range and diversity of data communications applications increase, the goals described by Fredrick R. Kappel, Board Chairman of the American Telephone and Telegraph Company will be fulfilled. The future of communications is best summarized in his own words:

"The pioneers of the telephone industry in its formative years looked ahead to universal service — to a time when anyone could talk to anyone else, anywhere, anytime. Today as we approach this goal, the word 'universal' begins to take on new meaning. We now see the word 'universal' as also meaning the exchange of information in any form that is desired. That form may be words, pictures, documents, handwriting or a host of machine languages. Universal communications will mean not only the ability to communicate with anyone, anywhere, anytime but in any form as well.

This, I believe, is the modern goal of our American communications industry — to provide universal communications of such nature, quality, and quantity that they will be unsurpassed in the world."

### Discussion Questions

1. Distinguish between "on-line" and "real-time" systems.
2. Discuss the future of data processing in its relationship to data communications.
3. What do you consider to be the most significant trend in the data communications field?
4. In light of the increase in applications of on-line real-time systems, what will be the future of batch processing operations?
5. Speculate as to what effect the computer and data communications will have on individuals for the next 10 to 15 years.

# KING CONSTRUCTION COMPANY

King Construction Company is a relatively young firm located in Louisville, Kentucky. The company has enjoyed rapid growth and after only ten years of operation has qualified to operate in 41 states, with its 1964 business exceeding $25 million. Projects consist primarily of motels, apartment buildings, shopping centers and industrial buildings, ranging in cost from three-quarters of a million to three million dollars.

About five years ago, at the beginning of its expansion period, the company developed an interest in electronic data processing and installed punched card equipment to process payrolls, cost reporting, accounts payable, and other administrative data.

All of the firm's business is procured through negotiation rather than by competitive bidding. In order to effectively negotiate for a project, the company must submit its proposal as soon as possible, while the prospect's interest in the project is still high. In 1960, the firm began considering a computer to expedite the preparation of proposals. At the same time it learned of the project planning method known at CPM—the Critical Path Method. Using this method, all jobs on a given project are charted to show the sequence that must be followed to achieve the shortest construction time and the lowest cost. A "critical" job is one that if delayed will delay the whole project. The "critical path" is the specific sequence of critical jobs.

Recognizing both the growing need for a quicker way to produce estimates and the advantages of the Critical Path Method of scheduling, King Construction installed a computer in its headquarters in 1963. The computer is equipped with random access storage. All construction job items have been catalogued, costed, and stored in the computer for use in estimating. The estimator assigns a code to each item. This code details the specifications and the construction method to be used. For example, concrete floor slabs are coded by type, reinforcing and other specifications and by the method of pouring and finishing. A batch of punched cards is prepared from the estimator's decisions — about 500 cards for the basic jobs on a million-dollar project. From these cards the computer generates some 5,000 cards to carry the complete information on all related operations. In this manner the computer dictates all of the tasks associated with a particular job, making it virtually impossible to overlook a single item. With this method, a firm proposal can be submitted to the prospect within 48 hours of the initial discussion. The same information, after being entered into cards, is used to produce the Critical Path Schedule.

King Construction is among the first construction firms in the country to use a computer for both estimating and scheduling.

For the Critical Path Method of scheduling to be fully effective, the Critical Path Schedule must be regularly updated as work on a project progresses. In order to accomplish this updating, a data communications system had to be developed that would be able to rapidly collect at the computer center in Louisville the necessary progress information from the company's many far-flung construction sites. A system was designed using card readers equipped with keyboards to transmit work progress information over regular long distance telephone service from the construction sites to Louisville.

On Friday afternoon each project superintendent reports the information necessary to update the schedule for his project to the home office. He has prepunched cards containing identifying information for each job on which work was performed during the week. On each card he notes his estimate of the time, in days and tenths of days, that will be required to complete the job. He places a regular long distance telephone call to Louisville and uses his card reader to transmit the report. This is done by placing each job card in the card reader which automatically transmits the prepunched identifying information to a card punch in Louisville. He then enters from the keyboard on his card reader the estimated number of days to completion as previously noted on the card. Any special explanations and discussion can be handled by throwing a switch that enables the superintendent to talk with the home office. He needs no clerical help to prepare the 20 cards that are normally involved in one week's work. All project reports are thus received by the home office before the end of the day each Friday.

On Saturday morning the data is electronically processed and each project is completely rescheduled — all the way to the estimated completion date. The revised schedules are airmailed to the construction sites Saturday afternoon so as to reach the superintendents by Monday morning.

The computer figures the costs of each project to date and, based on updated schedule information, predicts the final costs and profits.

It also gives the current overall financial position of the company. At the Louisville headquarters there is a control room where all project information is displayed: architect's sketches, progress photographs, updated Critical Path Charts, and the current cost and profit picture. Each Monday morning top management meets in the control room and reviews each project and the company as a whole. If a project's time, cost and profit figures are significantly above or below the estimates, an investigation is made to determine the cause and a course of action.

### Questions

1. What problem did the data communications system solve? How was it solved?
2. When did the progress information have to be at the computer site? Why was this schedule critical?
3. What advantage does it give the company to have weekly information on the progress of its jobs? How much is it worth in terms of dollars?

**Case II**

# CUSTER OIL COMPANY

Custer Oil Company, a refiner and distributor of fuel oils, was organized in 1933 by George and Harry Custer. Custer Oil buys crude oil which it refines to produce fuel oils and other by-products at its Philadelphia refinery. The fuel oils are supplied to distributors and industrial users from 15 terminals, with no direct residential sales handled by Custer Oil. Fuel oil sales make up the bulk of Custer Oil's business. There are no plans to open new terminals or refineries, and growth will come from further development of present territories. Custer Oil's fleet of oceangoing barges and tankers brings crude oil to Philadelphia from overseas and Gulf Coast points and delivers refined products to terminals located on the coast. Deliveries to inland terminals are normally made by railroad tank car.

General offices in Camden, New Jersey, are staffed by 200 employees. All administrative, accounting and buying functions are located there and operations at all locations are closely supervised from Camden. The 15 terminal locations are shown on the fact sheet. Each terminal has about 30 trucks, 1 dispatcher, 1 clerk, 3 watchmen and 32 drivers. Long distance service and two full-time WATS[1] lines are used extensively at Camden in the daily supervision of the terminals and in contacting other oil companies.

Custer Oil's biggest job, and the one on which the business was built, is providing fuel oil. The firm's trucks deliver from the terminals to its customers. The various terminals have been established so that each terminal handles approximately the same number of customers (about 800) and the same volume of fuel oil. The terminals operate from 8 A.M. to 5 P.M. and, except for emergencies, deliveries are made Monday through Friday only. Most deliveries are made in response to orders received at the terminal office by telephone with some deliveries made on a scheduled or "standing order" basis.

When an order is received, a clerk in the terminal office prepares a delivery ticket on a five-part form. (Figure 29, Page 106) The five copies are distributed as follows:

1. Gatehouse copy (kept by dispatcher)
2. Billing copy (sent to customer with invoice)
3. Inventory (for use at terminal)
4. Customer copy (left with customer)
5. Headquarter's copy (punched card stock)

A ticket number is preprinted on all copies of the ticket and is prepunched in the headquarters copy. Addressograph plates are used to enter the "Sold To" and "Delivered To" information and a "customer number" previously assigned by Custer Oil. The clerk imprints the information from the plate onto the ticket and enters in pencil the date and the number of gallons ordered.

The five-part delivery ticket is given to a dispatcher who enters the "vehicle number" on the ticket. The dispatcher has a loudspeaker system connected to the loading platforms over which he directs the loading of trucks. The trucks do not carry meters; entire trucks or individual compartments are used for each delivery. After the truck is loaded, the driver picks up the last four copies of the delivery tickets from the dispatcher. He leaves one copy of the ticket with the customer and returns the other three copies of the ticket, signed by the customer to the office after the delivery has been made.

At the end of the day the Billing and Headquarter's copies of the delivery ticket are sent to Camden by First Class Mail (Air Mail

[1] Wide Area Telephone Service (WATS) is discussed in the Supplementary Information Section.

from the most distant terminals). Average mailing cost for the tickets is $1.50 per day per terminal. The tickets arrive in Camden in one to three days. The tickets are then key-punched to add the 15 characters of variable information. This takes about 10 hours of total key punching time, or about $15 per day.

Billing is performed by the data processing center in Camden, and bills are usually sent to the customer the same day the tickets are received. The terms are net in 30 days, 2% in 10 days (counting from date of invoice). By long-established practice, Custer Oil has included a copy of delivery tickets with the bill, even though a copy was left with the customer at time of delivery. Although customers find this convenient, the practice could be discontinued if necessary. Deliveries average 2,000 per day, but since several deliveries may be billed to one customer the number of invoices is less: about 1,000 per day.

The general office operates from 9 A.M. to 5 P.M., and the data processing center functions from 7 A.M. to 10 P.M. The center has a medium-scale computer (with card reader, printer and two magnetic tape units) and other tab card equipment, including accounting machines, punches and two collators.

Custer Oil bills $22 million per month; on the basis of 22 working days in each month, its daily billing is $1,000,000. The present system of mailing delivery information requires an average of two days for transmission of accounts receivable information from the point of sale to the billing location. This means that at any point in time, more than $2 million of Custer Oil's operating capital is tied up in fuel oil that has already been delivered but has not yet been billed. Assuming that the cost of money to Custer is 6%, this $2 million is worth $10,000 per month or $120,000 annually before taxes. (The billing period to be granted customers and the resulting amount of working capital tied up in accounts receivable are determined as a policy decision. The lag in time between delivery and billing, however, does not stem from a policy decision but is the result of the rate at which bills can be prepared and sent out.)

### Define the Problem and Objectives

The delivery tickets take too long (1-3 days) to reach the data processing center at Camden.

A system should be designed that will speed up the movement of the delivery information from the terminals to the data processing center.

## Analyze the Facts

*Distribution* — Although there are probably other types of information flowing between the various points in the system, only one type is described in this case. This information is the delivery ticket information that is sent from each of the 15 terminals to the data processing center at Camden. *(Figure 28.)*

| TO / FROM | CAMDEN | 15 TERMINALS |
|---|---|---|
| CAMDEN | | |
| 15 TERMINALS | Delivery ticket information | |

Figure 28. Distribution chart for Custer Oil Company.

*Volume* — The supplementary information at the end of this case lists 21 characters of information about each delivery that must be sent to Camden. It also indicates that on the average each terminal makes 133 deliveries per day. Therefore, the total number of characters received at Camden is:

$$
\begin{array}{r}
21 \text{ characters per delivery} \\
\times\, 133 \text{ deliveries per day} \\
\hline
2,793 \text{ characters per terminal} \\
\times\quad 15 \text{ terminals} \\
\hline
41,895 \text{ characters per day}
\end{array}
$$

*Urgency* — Under the existing system, the cards arrive at the data processing center one to three days (average is two days) after the oil is delivered. Ideally the delivery information should get to the data processing center the day of delivery and early enough to be processed and to allow invoices to be mailed that day. Preparing and dating the invoices the day of delivery would cut the billing period by an average of two days. (The two-day lag in billing does not fall within the 30-day payment period but represents an additional delay resulting from the

slowness of getting the billing information to the data processing center for preparation of the invoices.)

*Language* — The information at the data processing center should
be in punch card form. Conversion can be done if another
form of the information is thought necessary at the terminals,
but this will entail additional cost. If additional transmission
speed can be obtained, however, the additional conversion cost
may be offset.

*Accuracy* — Since the information being received at Camden is in
the form of random digits, some type of error detection and
correction system seems justified if the cost is not too high.

*Cost* — Two types of cost must be considered: The cost in the old
system that can be eliminated or reduced and the cost of the
new system.

A. Old system costs to be saved:

  1. $10,000/month, reduction in cost of money on $2 mil-
     lion reduction in accounts receivable.
  2. $495/month mailing cost from terminals ($1.50/day x
     22 working days/month x 15 terminals=$495/month.)
  3. $330/month of key punching cost at Camden. ($15/day
     22 working days/month = $330/month.) (See note)

     Since the data must still be keyed in all three of the
     systems, described later, the keypunching cost saved
     at Camden is offset by the keying cost at the terminals.
     NOTE: For simplification only actual, not loaded, wage costs are shown.

B. New system costs: To be developed by the student in the
   solution of the case.

PROBLEM: Using the preceding information as the basis of the
system's requirements, analyze the following three solutions to
determine which one best satisfies the requirement described
above.

### Design Alternative Systems Determine the Costs

These two steps have been performed for you in this case. Three
different systems have been designed and the basic costs of the
system components have been listed.

The problem in this case is to evaluate these three solutions.
Read these three alternate solutions carefully, calculate the total
cost of each, evaluate them as described in the next section, and
then select the one which best satisfies the conditions of the problem.

102

## System A

A low-speed card reader with DATA-PHONE Service[2] could be located at each of the terminals, with two low-speed receiving card punches and DATA-PHONE Service at Camden. Prepunched cards containing the ticket number and the customer number would be supplied to the terminals. Each evening the data processing center could call the terminals by using the two existing WATS lines. These lines would be available since only the data processing center operates after 5 P.M. Upon being called from the data processing center, an attendant at the terminal could place the prepunched card for each of the day's deliveries into the card reader and automatically transmit the ticket number and customer number. The attendant would then manually key in the variable information-terminal number, product code and gallons delivered. This information would be received in punched card form on the receiving card punch at Camden.

The average time required to transmit one prepunched card and key in eight characters of variable information would be about 17 seconds. The card reader-receiving card punch system provides some check for transmission errors occurring in transmission. It does not provide any type of printed document at the source to be used as a means of visually checking input errors in the variable information. The charge for a typical card reader is $15 per month, and the associated DATA-PHONE data set costs $5 per month. A receiving card punch costs about $95 per month, with $43 per month for the associated DATA-PHONE data set. The charge for each WATS line is $700 per month. If an existing WATS line is used to call the terminals between 5 P.M. and 10 P.M., a proportion of the monthly cost of $700 per line would be allocable to this operation, even though the "out-of-pocket" costs for the WATS line would remain the same.

### Things to keep in mind:

1.  With a requirement of 17 seconds to transmit each card, how long will it take to transmit all cards at each terminal? How long will it take for Camden to receive all cards from all terminals on two receiving card punches?

2.  How long will each WATS line be used for data transmission? What proportion of the monthly cost should be charged to this data use?

3.  The low-speed card reader requires an attendant at the send-

---

[2] DATA-PHONE Service is discussed in the Supplementary Information Section.

ing location during transmission. An attendant would also be required at Camden during transmission to call the terminals, load and unload cards, etc. This would require about two hours' time per night. What is the total personnel time at all locations which will be required to perform one day's total transmission?

## System B

A medium-speed automatic punch card transmitter with an associated DATA-PHONE data set could be used in each terminal, and the compatible receiver in the data processing center at Camden. The 21 characters of billing information for each of the day's deliveries could be key-punched into 80 column cards, using the same card transmitter at the terminals. The cards, one for each delivery, could then be sent from the transmitters at the terminals to the receiver at Camden. Using existing WATS, transmission could occur after 5 p.m. from Camden. Camden would call each location using its existing WATS line.

The rate at which an automatic card transmitter with DATA-PHONE Service transmits 80 column cards with 21 columns punched is 22 cards per minute. The receiver will check the data for transmission errors. The charge for the card transmitter receiver is $215 per month, and the associated DATA-PHONE data set costs $25 per month. As in System "A" above, if an existing WATS line is used, a portion of the monthly charges should be allocated to this operation.

### Things to keep in mind:

1. With a transmission rate of 22 cards per minute, how long will it take to transmit all cards at each terminal? How long will it take for Camden to receive all cards from all terminals?

2. The card transmitter-receiver requires an attendant at both the sending and the receiving locations during transmission. How much personnel time will be required to perform one day's total transmission?

## System C

Each terminal could install a keyboard printer equipped with a paper tape reader and punch. The information from the delivery tickets would be typed on the keyboard and punched into paper tape simultaneously. Using the tape reader, this paper tape could then be transmitted using a teleprinter exchange type of service from the terminals to the Camden office. The Camden office would have an on-line tape-to-card converter in addition to their keyboard printer. This device, a card punch connected to a keyboard printer, would receive the teleprinter line signals and convert them to punched cards. This arrangement changes the language of the data from punched paper tape to punched card in the process of receiving the data. The keyboard printer with an automatic punched paper tape reader transmits at a rate of 10 characters per second. However, in transmitting from a keyboard printer to a card punch, 10 additional characters must be added to the 21 characters required in each card. These 10 characters do not contain meaningful information and serve only as buffering characters to allow the card punch time to feed another card. The need to key in the buffer characters will increase the preparation time somewhat. The keyboard printer and receiving card punch arrangement offers page copy for visual error checking (especially for input), but no machine checking for transmission errors is available.

A keyboard printer, equipped with a tape punch and reader, costs $60 per month. The on-line tape-to-card converter arrangement at Camden would cost $265 per month. The transmission charges for this system would be about $425 per month using a teleprinter exchange type of service.

### Things to keep in mind:

1. With a transmission rate of 10 characters per second how long will it take to transmit all billing information at each terminal? How long will it take to receive all billing information from all terminals at Camden? Remember that 10 characters must be added to the 21 characters on each delivery ticket to allow for buffering.

2. The keyboard printer can be arranged for unattended sending. The attendant can place prepunched tape into the reader before leaving work. The tape reader, upon being called from Camden, would automatically begin transmitting. How much personnel time would be required for transmission with this arrangement?

### Evaluate the Systems

In the evaluation of each system design, four major areas should be considered. These four areas are discussed in detail in Chapter V, but are listed here for convenience.

1. How well does each system solve the problem?
2. How well does each system meet the specifications?
3. What does each system cost?

4. What other benefits does each system provide, either tangible or intangible?

## Supplementary Information for Custer Oil

### FACT SHEET

Volumes—

    Number of characters per delivery:

| | | |
|---|---|---|
| ticket number | — | 6 characters |
| customer number | — | 7 characters |
| product number | — | 1 character |
| terminal number | — | 2 characters |
| gallons | — | 5 characters |
| total | — | 21 characters per delivery |

Miscellaneous Data—

| | Total Company | Each Terminal |
|---|---|---|
| Customers | 12,000 | 800 |
| Deliveries per day | 2,000 | 133 |
| Invoices per day | 1,000 | 67 |
| Monthly billing | $22,000,000 | $1,467,000 |
| Daily billing (22-day month) | $1,000,000 | $66,700 |
| Value per delivery | $500 | $500 |
| Value per invoice | $1,000 | $1,000 |

Locations—

| | | |
|---|---|---|
| General offices | Camden, N. J. | Johnstown, Pa. |
| Refinery | Philadelphia, Pa. | Lancaster, Pa. |
| Terminals | Albany, N. Y. | Pittsburgh, Pa. |
| | Buffalo, N. Y. | Scranton, Pa. |
| | Elmira, N. Y. | Williamsport, Pa. |
| | Syracuse, N. Y. | York, Pa. |
| | Utica, N. Y. | Georgetown, Del. |
| | Allentown, Pa. | Wilmington, Del. |
| | Erie, Pa. | |

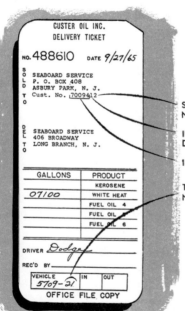

Figure 29. Five part delivery ticket for Custer Oil Company.

# FRANKLIN DEPARTMENT STORES

Franklin is a fast-growing retail department store chain. The general offices are in Boston, Massachusetts, with a warehouse at Chicago, Illinois, and 22 stores located throughout the eastern and central part of the nation (see supplementary information at end of case).

Franklin does a high-volume cash and carry business with a low markup on merchandise. Its 1962 gross sales were $65 million, with a 2.3% net profit. The inventory turns over at a rate of about seven times per year. The stores operate on a self-service basis and the items are brought to checkout counters for wrapping and payment.

Control of the Franklin chain is centralized at headquarters. A group of 20 buyers has the responsibility for all merchandising. The buyers are located in New York to place them close to their vendors.

Franklin stores carry about 10,000 items in stock. About 20% of these are called control items. Control items are the faster moving or more expensive items and represent 30% of Franklin's total item volume and 40% of the total dollar volume. Since these control items are usually not brand name products and therefore require examination and selection at a vendor's sales room, they are centrally purchased by the buyers in New York.

The remaining 8,000 non-control items are handled by the store managers under the general supervision of the buyers. These non-control items are broken into five categories:

1. Local purchases — Candys, etc., are items over which the store managers have full purchasing responsibility.
2. Drugs and Cosmetics — These items are stocked by a central warehouse in Chicago, and managers place orders for these items on an "as needed" basis. These are the only items that Franklin warehouses. All order processing, inventory records and statistical reports for these items are handled at the warehouse.
3. Standing Orders — Staple items are shipped automatically by vendors on the basis of standing orders placed by buyers. Store managers adjust their changing requirements through buyers.

4. Distributor Servicing — Salesmen from various distributors visit stores at regular intervals to check inventories and replenish stocks.

5. Concession Departments — Certain departments, such as shoes, lunch counters, and millinery, are leased to outside operators on a percent-of-profit basis. These departments have their own separate cash registers.

In order to maintain control over merchandise movement, the buyers utilize a monthly sales report on non-control items and a weekly sales report on control items.

## Monthly Report for Non-Control Items

The monthly report for non-control items is derived from detailed sales records kept by department managers on standard forms. These records reflect the number of items on hand and the number of items sold in each category during the month. The departmental reports are consolidated by the store managers and the monthly store reports are mailed directly to the buyers.

## Weekly Report for Control Items

When a buyer makes a purchase of a control item he gives the vendor one purchase order which indicates the proper distribution of the merchandise to each store. He sends a copy of the purchase order to each store involved, noting on the copies the selling price for each item on the order. He also sends a copy of the purchase order to the Boston headquarters, where the information is key-punched for updating the "on order" information in the inventory file.

When the merchandise ordered is received at the stores, it is checked against their copy of the order. The vendor sends an individual invoice to each store, which is approved by the store and mailed to Boston for payment. After the merchandise has been checked against the order, a price tag is printed. A punched tag is prepared on a print punch machine and both are affixed to each control item (see *Figure 31*, page 113, for a picture of the tag.) A tag print punch machine is a device that produces punch-coded and printed merchandise tags. In this case, eight columns of coded information are entered on each tag. The information recorded by these punched holes can be machine-read for rapid processing of the inventory information.

This punching (not including preparing the price tag) requires a clerk for one hour per day per store. When a control item is sold, the girl at the checkout counter removes the lower half of the tag (the coded punched portion) and places it in a receptacle. Once each day the tags are collected from each checkout counter, bundled and air-mailed to Boston for processing.

When the tags are received at Boston they are manicured[1] and placed in one of six tag readers.[2] These tag readers are associated with two summary punches. The summary punches enter the information from the tags into punched cards. The rate of conversion from tag to card is 100 tags per minute per tag reader or with three tag readers working with each summary punch, 600 tags per minute. The manicuring and converting of tags requires five girls on a full-time basis at Boston. The tag readers cost $200 per month each and the summary punches cost $85 per month each. Each day the cards are read into a computer for updating a master inventory tape that contains past sales records for each control item for each store. On Wednesday a printout is made showing the following information by items and by store:

1. How many on hand
2. How many on order
3. How many sold this week
4. How many sold last four weeks
5. How many sold same week last year

The printout contains about 600,000 characters and is several hundred pages long. It is mailed to New York and is in the buyer's hands on Thursday morning. The report includes sales made through the previous Monday (see mail schedule in supplementary information).

This report is the most essential tool in Franklin's operational control. It indicates to the buyers which items are moving well in certain stores, which items are not moving well in certain stores, and inventory levels and sales on each item both by individual store and for the total company. Based on the information in this report, the buyers transfer goods from one store to another, avail themselves of special purchases based on product movement trends, and control out-of-stock and over-stock inventory levels.

In analyzing the report, the buyers first look for those items that have had either an appreciable increase or an appreciable decrease of sales in any store. This information is called "exception information" and would be quite valuable to the buyers on a daily basis for

---

[1] Manicuring is a process whereby merchandise tags are manually trimmed with scissors to facilitate their handling and accurate reading in a tag reader.
[2] Tag readers read the punched holes in the tags and generate the proper code for a card punch, which in turn produces a punched card.

the previous day's sales. The exception information constitutes about 10% of the total report, or 60,000 characters per week. The remaining 540,000 characters of the report are used to maintain long-range inventory levels and are adequately provided on a weekly basis.

Franklin has a full-time WATS[3] line that is used to handle voice traffic between Boston and the stores. This line is used extensively from 8 to 12 A.M. and from 1 to 5 P.M., Monday through Friday, for administrative voice messages between the headquarters and the stores. The monthly cost is $1,400.

Determine the primary problem in Franklin's present inventory control procedure. Analyze the various data and design a data communications system that will solve Franklin's problems. The following outline will aid in the analysis of the data.

### Define the Problem and Objectives

What is the problem that Franklin faces? What specific area of Franklin's information flow needs improvement? How can it be improved? What should be the objective of any new system?

### Analyze the Facts

*Distribution* — Where does the information originate and where does it go? Use the following chart as a guide. (Since the information from all 22 stores is the same, it may be combined on the chart.)

| FROM \ TO | HEADQUARTERS (Boston) | BUYERS (New York) | 22 STORES |
|---|---|---|---|
| HEADQUARTERS (Boston) | | | |
| BUYERS (New York) | | | |
| 22 STORES | | | |

Figure 30. Distribution chart for Franklin Department Stores.

---

[3] Wide Area Telephone Service (WATS) is discussed in the Supplementary Information Section.

*Volume* — 1.  How many daily transactions per store?

2.  How many items per transaction?

3.  How many items per store per day?

4.  How many of these are control items?

5.  If a daily sales report on control items were to be prepared
    a.  How many characters per control item would have to be sent to Boston?  (Assume that no control or buffer characters are needed.)
    b.  How many characters per store per day would have to be sent to Boston?
    c.  How many characters would have to be received at Boston daily from all 22 stores?

6.  How many characters are now received at New York weekly?

7.  How many characters of exceptional information would the buyers like to receive at New York daily?  (Assume that one sixth of the weekly exception information is sent each day.)

8.  Calculate the time required to receive all item information at Boston.  (Assume a 100-character-per-second transmission speed.)

9.  Calculate the time required to send exception information from Boston to New York daily.  (Assume 10-character-per-second transmission speed.)

10.  Make a simple geographic diagram showing the main locations in the system and the direction of the important information flow between them.

*Urgency* — What information do the New York buyers want daily? How current should it be to be meaningful (same day, next day, etc.)?
What information do New York buyers want weekly?  How current must it be?
What information does Boston need daily to supply the information the buyers want?  How current must it be?

*Language* — What possible languages could be available at the stores (such as tags, punched card, paper tape, magnetic tape)?
What language(s) does the computer need at Boston?
In which form is the information needed at New York?

*Accuracy* — Assume that no error detection or correction (EDC) is needed.

## Design the System

Make a block diagram showing the proposed system. (Design only one system.) Label the blocks and show the language of the information at each point.

> Hint: Use a 100 character per second paper tape sender at each store and one receiver at Boston. Use teleprinters and *Data-Phone* Service to send information to New York.

| | | |
|---|---|---|
| Paper tape sender | $155.00/mo. | (incl. data set) |
| Paper tape receiver | $185.00/mo. | (incl. data set) |
| Keyboard printer with | | |
|    tape reader | $ 70.00/mo. | (incl. data set) |
| Keyboard printer | $ 60.00/mo. | (incl. data set) |

## Determine the Costs

In determining the total cost of the new data communications system the following costs should be considered:

1. Communications terminal equipment
2. Other equipment
3. Transmission (Determine how long the WATS line is used for this transmission each day and allocate that portion of the cost of the service to this use)
4. Personnel

## Evaluate the System

Since only one system was designed, no comparison of several systems is necessary and only the other benefits have to be evaluated.

Is there any saving over the old system in terms of operating costs? Determine what costs in the old system will be eliminated or reduced by installing the new system.

1. How much personnel cost is presently involved in punching tags at the 22 stores monthly? (Assume 30 working days/month.)
2. How much personnel cost is presently involved in converting tags at Boston monthly? (Assume 4⅓ weeks/month.)
3. What is present transmission cost? (Assume 30 days/month.)
4. What is present equipment cost for the tag system? Are there any benefits that will result from the use of this system? Do they appear to justify the cost of the new system?

## FACT SHEET 1

Mail Schedule —

*Monday through Friday*

Tags from previous day's sales are airmailed from the stores in midafternoon and arrive at Boston either the next day or early on the second day depending on the location of the store.

*Saturday*

Tags for Friday and Saturday are airmailed after the store has closed on Saturday and arrive in Boston on Monday morning.

*Sunday*

Tags are airmailed first thing Monday morning and arrive at Boston Tuesday morning.

The above schedule results in both Friday's and Saturday's tags being converted on Monday, and both Sunday's and Monday's tags being converted on Tuesday.

Air mail costs are $1.00 per day per store.

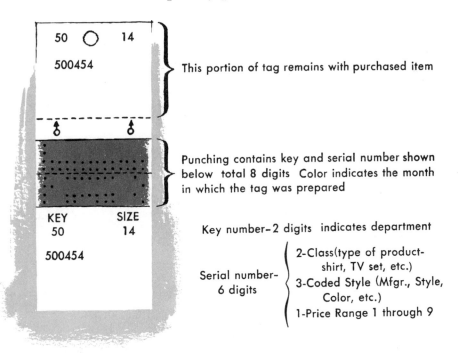

Figure 31. Merchandise tag for Franklin Department Stores.

## Supplementary Information for
## Franklin Department Stores (Continued)

### FACT SHEET 2

Store Operations —

Each store has about 100 employees. The stores are open from 9 A.M. to 10 P.M. on Monday through Saturday and from 1 P.M. to 10 P.M. on Sunday. Each store operates on a self-service basis and has ten checkout positions equipped with cash registers. Franklin leases the cash registers, which cost about $60 per month each. They are the type of cash register to which a point-of-sale paper tape recording punch[4] can be added. The cost for the tape punch is another $15 monthly per cash register.

Each store also has one tag punch which it leases for $80 per month.

Checkout clerks (who also do the tag punching) are paid about $50 per week (5 days/week, 8 hours/day).

Each store averages 2,400 sales per day, with an average of six items per sale.

### FACT SHEET 3

Data Processing Operation at Boston —
( SEE NOTE PAGE 102)

*Day Shift*

| 3 Computer Operators | $ 65 per week |
| 2 Programmers | 150 per week |
| 5 "Manicurists"-General Clerks | 50 per week (5 days/week) |
| 6 Keypunch Operators | 50 per week (5 days/week) |

*Evening Shift*

| 1 Computer Operator | $ 85 per week |
| 3 Keypunch Operators | 60 per week (5 days/week) |

*Equipment*

- 7 Keypunches (non-printing)
- 1 Keypunch (printing)
- 2 Gang Summary Punches (associated with Tag Readers)
- 6 Tag Readers
- 1 Medium Size Computer
- 1 900 Line Per Minute Printer

---

[4] A point-of-sale recording tape punch can record in punched paper tape selected information from any transaction keyed on the cash register.

FACT SHEET 3 (continued)

1 800 Card Per Minute Reader
1 Paper Tape Reader for input to computer (ASCII code)[5]
1 Paper Tape Punch for output from computer (ASCII code)

The Data Processing Center operates two shifts (a day and evening shift), Monday through Saturday.

FACT SHEET 4

Franklin Department Stores

Store Locations —

| Store No. | City |
|---|---|
| 1 | Boston, Mass. |
| 2 | Providence, R. I. |
| 3 | Hartford, Conn. |
| 4 | Chicago, Ill. |
| 5 | Hammond, Ind. |
| 6 | Louisville, Ky. |
| 7 | Dayton, Ohio |
| 8 | Lansing, Mich. |
| 9 | Rochester, N. Y. |
| 10 | Richmond, Va. |
| 11 | Detroit, Mich. |
| 12 | Akron, Ohio |
| 13 | Marion, Ohio |
| 14 | Battle Creek, Mich. |
| 15 | Saginaw, Mich. |
| 16 | Nashville, Tenn. |
| 17 | Syracuse, N. Y. |
| 18 | Springfield, Ill. |
| 19 | Atlanta, Ga. |
| 20 | Rockford, Ill. |
| 21 | Canton, Ohio |
| 22 | Lowell, Mass. |

---

[5] See glossary for definition.

# SUPPLEMENTARY INFORMATION

**Data Transmission Terminal Equipment**
**Communication Services**
**Communication Switching**
**Glossary of Data Communications Terms**
**Data Communications Bibliography**

### Introduction

This supplementary section is divided into five sections:

Data Transmission Terminal Equipment
Communication Services
Communication Switching
Glossary of Data Communications Terms
Data Communications Bibliography

The information contained in the Terminal, Service and Switching sections is not intended to be a complete review of all the many facets of data communications. Its purpose is to provide an appreciation of the terminal equipment, communication services and switching techniques associated with the transmission of data. These sections are referred to a number of times in the text where additional information will prove helpful.

The terminal equipment described here is also only representative of what is commercially available. At the present time, there are many different types and models of business machines compatible with communication services. For more detailed information about data communication terminal equipment, an excellent source is *Office Automation* (see bibliography). Additional information about specific terminal equipment can be obtained from the manufacturer or supplier of the equipment.

The communication services described here are generally available from the communication common carriers and from suppliers of privately owned microwave systems. There are, of course, many other communication services available but the ones described here are considered to be of particular interest to students concerned with a study of data communications. More detailed information can be obtained from the suppliers.

The switching techniques discussed are basic to an understanding of how messages are moved through the communication sub-system of an information system.

The glossary has been largely limited to terms associated with data communications. Some data processing terms have been included where it was felt that they were necessary to a better understanding of data communications.

The bibliography is also limited to books and articles relating to data communications, but some references have been included in the field of systems planning since this area is of great importance in data communications.

# DATA
# TRANSMISSION TERMINAL
# EQUIPMENT

### Data Sets

Communication channels are used to convey data between business machines. But these channels are frequently not capable of transmitting the electrical signals generated by business machines. A data set is used, therefore, to convert the business machine signals into tones, which can be transmitted over communication facilities. At the receiving end, a similar data set accepts the transmitted tones, reconverts them back to electrical signals, and delivers these signals to the business machine. *(Figure 32.)*

Figure 32. A data set converts the electrical signal of a business machine into tones for transmission over communication lines.

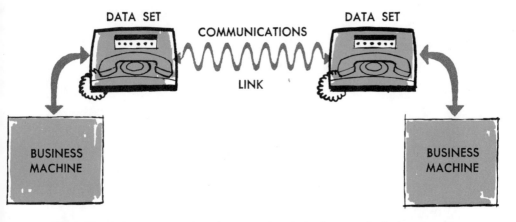

Figure 33. A data set is used as the connecting device between the business machine and the communication link.

Data sets can not only convert business machine signals into tones the communication channels can handle but also provide a means for dialing and setting up the connection. *(Figure 33.)*

Data sets can be used with many different types of business machine terminals. The remainder of this section will be devoted to a description of these terminals.

### Keyboard-Only Devices

Keyboard-only devices are generally used to transmit data to a data-gathering device such as a computer or card punch. The pushbutton telephone is a good example of a keyboard-only device. The pushbutton telephone differs from older model telephones in that it has pushbuttons instead of a dial with 10 fingerholes. These pushbuttons generate tones that are used to direct the call through the telephone network. *(Figure 34.)*

To place a call, the buttons are pressed corresponding to the desired telephone number (just as in dialing the call by means of the rotary dial.) Each button transmits a different pair of tones representing the numbers 1 to 0. After the call has been established the telephone can be used to carry on a conversation or to send data by means of the pushbuttons. This is possible because the tones from the buttons are readily transmitted through the telephone network. This signaling to the distant end using the pushbuttons on the telephone is called "end-to-end signaling."

For example, a call is placed from a pushbutton telephone to a receiving data set connected to a card punch. The receiving data

Figure 34. The card dialer telephone permits automatic dialing by using punched plastic cards. In this model which uses audible tones for dialing, pushbuttons are used instead of the rotary dial. Data may also be punched in the cards and transmitted by these new phones to computers and other business machines.

set automatically answers the call, sends back an answer tone and connects the card punch to the line. As the buttons on the telephone are pressed, the tones are transmitted over the line to the receiving data set. The data set converts the tones to electrical signals and relays the signals to the card punch which punches holes in a card, thereby reproducing the original data entered at the telephone. Keyboard devices are generally designed to operate as fast as a person can operate the keys.

### Keyboard Printers

A keyboard printer is a particular type of teleprinter equipment. (*Figure 35.*) It is quite similar to a normal typewriter in that it has a keyboard consisting of alphabetic, numeric and function keys, and a printing mechanism. In addition, however, it has a signal generator that generates electrical signals. The signals are coded to conform with the characters represented on the keyboard. (*Figure 36.*) As the operator types a character, a coded signal is generated

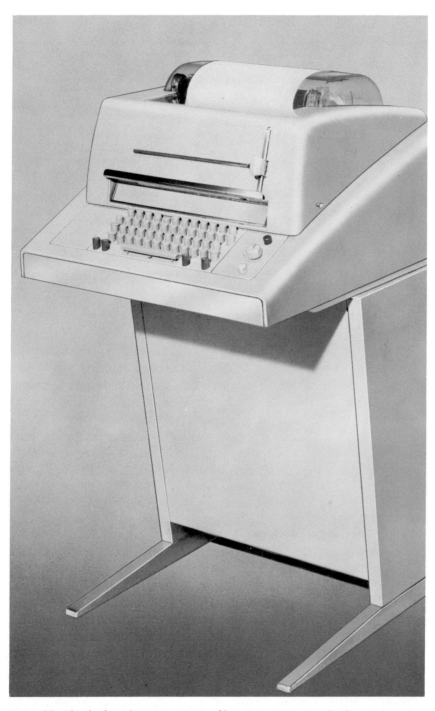

Figure 35. This keyboard printer operates like a typewriter. As the keys are used to print a message, coded signals go out on the communications line to print the identical message at a distant machine.

Figure 36. The keyboards of many teleprinters are almost identical to those found on standard office typewriters.

and transmitted over a communication channel to a receiving teleprinter.

At the receiving end, the coded signal is interpreted and the character is printed. Two or more operators at teleprinters connected on the same circuit can converse simply by typing back and forth. *(Figure 37.)*

Some teleprinters can also produce punched paper tape. As the operator types a character, a coded signal activates the tape punch, which punches holes in the paper tape. These holes represent the particular character that was typed (*Figure* 38, page 124) in a coded form.

### Punched Paper
### Tape Transmission Terminals

Punched paper tape transmission terminals consist of two units — a sender and a receiver. These units enable data recorded as holes punched in paper tape to be transmitted over communication facilities. *(Figure 39.)*

The sender consists of a paper tape reader and a signal generator. As the tape passes through the reader, the holes punched in the tape are read by sensing pins that are connected to the signal generator. The presence of a hole in the tape is sensed by a pin, and an electrical signal is generated by the signal generator. The absence of a hole indicates that no electrical signal should be generated. The signal generator sends the signals to a data set for transmission over the communication channel.

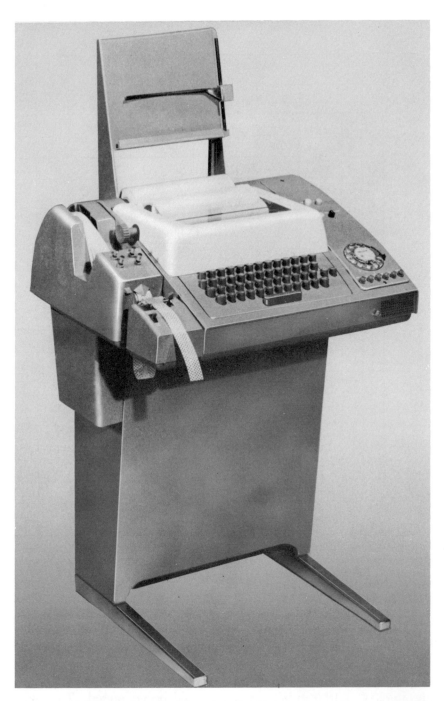

Figure 37. This automatic send and receive teleprinter can be used to send messages either by keyboard or prepunched paper tape. It also receives messages in punched paper tape or page copy. Tape can be punched from the keyboard for later transmission.

123

| b7 → | | | | | 0 | 0 | 0 | 0 | 1 | 1 | 1 | 1 |
| b6 → | | | | | 0 | 0 | 1 | 1 | 0 | 0 | 1 | 1 |
| Bits b5 → | | | | | 0 | 1 | 0 | 1 | 0 | 1 | 0 | 1 |
| $b_4$ | $b_3$ | $b_2$ | $b_1$ | Col.→ Row ↓ | 0 | 1 | 2 | 3 | 4 | 5 | 6 | 7 |
|---|---|---|---|---|---|---|---|---|---|---|---|---|
| 0 | 0 | 0 | 0 | 0 | NUL | DLE | SP | 0 | \ | P | @ | p |
| 0 | 0 | 0 | 1 | 1 | SOH | DC1 | ! | 1 | A | Q | a | q |
| 0 | 0 | 1 | 0 | 2 | STX | DC2 | " | 2 | B | R | b | r |
| 0 | 0 | 1 | 1 | 3 | ETX | DC3 | # | 3 | C | S | c | s |
| 0 | 1 | 0 | 0 | 4 | EOT | DC4 | $ | 4 | D | T | d | t |
| 0 | 1 | 0 | 1 | 5 | ENQ | NAK | % | 5 | E | U | e | u |
| 0 | 1 | 1 | 0 | 6 | ACK | SYN | & | 6 | F | V | f | v |
| 0 | 1 | 1 | 1 | 7 | BEL | ETB | ' | 7 | G | W | g | w |
| 1 | 0 | 0 | 0 | 8 | BS | CAN | ( | 8 | H | X | h | x |
| 1 | 0 | 0 | 1 | 9 | HT | EM | ) | 9 | I | Y | i | y |
| 1 | 0 | 1 | 0 | 10 | LF | SS | * | : | J | Z | j | z |
| 1 | 0 | 1 | 1 | 11 | VT | ESC | + | ; | K | ] | k | { |
| 1 | 1 | 0 | 0 | 12 | FF | FS | , | < | L | ~ | l | ⌐ |
| 1 | 1 | 0 | 1 | 13 | CR | GS | − | = | M | [ | m | } |
| 1 | 1 | 1 | 0 | 14 | SO | RS | . | < | N | Λ | n | I |
| 1 | 1 | 1 | 1 | 15 | SI | US | / | ? | O | — | o | DEL |

Figure 38. The American Standard Code for Information Interchange (ASCII) was developed as the standard code for the interchange of information between data processing and communication systems. Shown here is the proposed revision of ASCII now in the final stages of A.S.A. approval.

At the receiver the operation is reversed. The receiver consists of a signal interpreter and a paper tape punch. As the electrical signals are received from the data set or the communication channel, the pins in the tape punch are activated and punch holes in paper tape. The presence of an electrical signal activates a pin and a hole is punched. In the absence of an electrical signal, no hole is punched. These terminals are designed to operate at speeds of 10 to 300 characters per second.

Compatible DATA-PHONE data set and System 108 Transmitter

Compatible DATA-PHONE data set and System 208 Receiver

Figure 39. The Tally Corporation's Systems 108 and 208 transmit punched paper tape at a speed of 600 words per minute.

## Punched Card
## Transmission Terminals

Punched card transmission terminals enable data recorded as holes punched in a card to be transmitted over communication channels. The sending and receiving units are separate pieces of equipment. *(Figure 40.)*

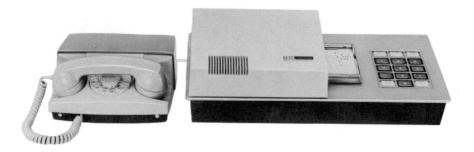

Figure 40. The IBM 1001 Data Transmission Terminal will read punched cards and also accept a keyboard entry of variable information. The receiving terminal punches cards containing all the information sent from the card reader. This equipment will operate over voice grade communication channels. It is shown with compatible DATA-PHONE data set.

The sender consists of a punched card reader and a signal generator. As a card passes through the reader, the holes punched in the card are read by sensing pins that are connected to the signal generator. The presence of a hole in a card is sensed by a pin, and an electrical pulse is generated by the signal generator. The absence of a hole indicates that no electrical signal should be generated. The signal generator sends the signals to a data set for transmission.

At the receiver the operation is reversed. The receiver consists of a signal interpreter and a card punch. As the electrical signals are received from the data set, the pins in the card punch are activated and punch holes in a card. The presence of an electrical signal activates a pin and a hole is punched. In the absence of an electrical signal, no hole is punched. These terminals operate at speeds varying from about 12 to 300 characters per second, depending primarily upon whether the cards are fed in manually (as in the picture) or automatically.

## Magnetic Tape
## Transmission Terminals

Magnetic tape transmission terminals enable data recorded on magnetic tape to be transmitted over communication facilities.

A terminal has the ability to send or receive. It consists of a read-write head and a signal generator capable of either transmitting or receiving. *(Figure 41.)*

Data is recorded on tape as magnetized spots located in parallel tracks along the length of the tape. As the tape passes over the head for sending (reading), the magnetized spots generate electrical pulses that are converted to coded signals and transmitted by a data set over a communication line to the receiver.

At the receiving location, the coded signals are received by a data set, converted to electrical pulses and delivered to the magnetic tape unit, which writes on the tape by magnetizing spots to correspond to the character received.

Figure 41. The RCA Model 5907 Magnetic Tape Terminal can transmit information at speeds of 150, 300 or even 62,500 characters per second depending upon the data set and communications channel used.

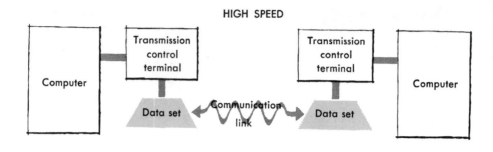

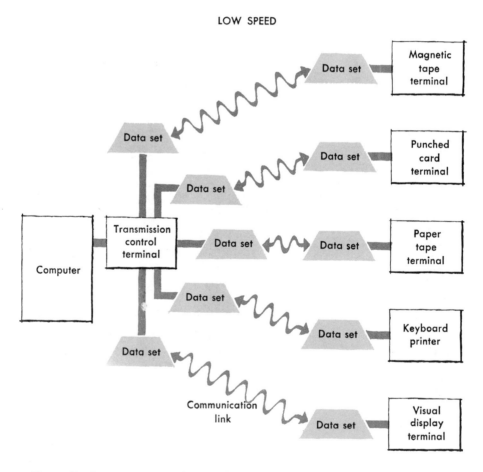

Figure 42. Transmission control terminals permit a computer to communicate with a variety of remote terminals.

## Computer
## Transmission Control Terminals

A computer transmission control terminal permits a computer system to be used for data transmission in addition to its data processing function.

When transmitting, the terminal converts the language of the computer into signals suitable for transmission with a data set. When receiving, the terminal converts signals received from the data set back to the proper language of the computer.

Since computers operate at high speeds, it would be costly in terms of computer usage to tie these computers up for the transmission of data at relatively low or medium speeds. To counteract this, some transmission control terminals are equipped with buffers. Buffers are memory units that receive data from a computer at high speed, store the data, convert the data to the proper code, and slow the data down to the transmission speed required by the receiving equipment or communication service. This operation is reversed when data transmission flows from a low-speed device to a computer.

Computer transmission control terminals are designed to operate at speeds varying from as slow as a person pushing buttons on a telephone to as fast as 62,500 characters per second. *Figure 42* illustrates some of the more common arrangements when computer transmission control terminals are used.

It is also possible to connect computers directly together so that they can exchange information at very high rates of speed. By using several wide band communication channels, information may be exchanged at main frame speeds. These arrangements are expensive, however, and the benefits of the total system must make the cost worthwhile.

## Handwriting
## Transmission Terminals

Handwriting transmission terminals transmit written messages or sketches over communication lines. *(Figure 43.)*

The message originating at the transmitter is written with a ballpoint pen on regular paper. As the pen moves on the paper, varying tones are generated and transmitted by means of the data set over a communication line to the receiving data set and its associated receiving business machine. There the tones are interpreted and the receiving pen reproduces the handwritten copy.

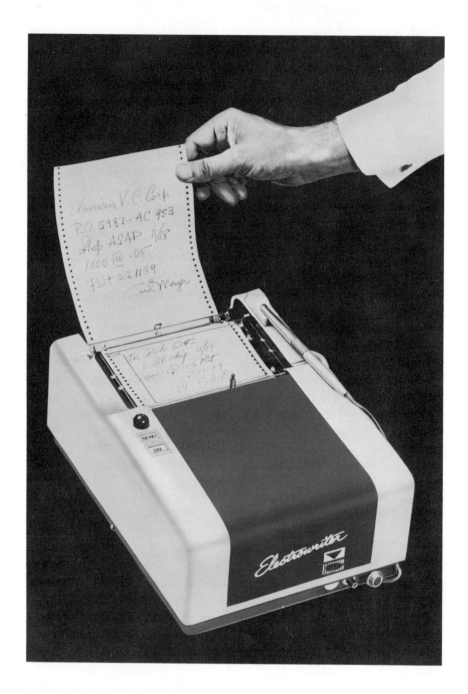

Figure 43. The Victor Electrowriter transceiver sends and receives handwritten messages and sketches via communications channels.

## Fascimile Terminals

Facsimile terminals are basically duplicating devices. These terminals can scan a document at a sending location and reproduce the document at a remote receiving location miles away. (*Figure 44.*)

The transmitting facsimile terminal converts black and white spaces on a document to electrical signals. Communication lines equipped with data sets carry these signals to a receiving facsimile terminal where the black and white spaces are duplicated. Some facsimile terminals are used to transmit only black and white material. Other terminals are capable of also reproducing shades of gray, thus permitting half-tone pictures to be transmitted. Facsimile terminals are available to operate at speeds from one page (8½ x 11) in six minutes to 16 pages (8½ x 11) per minute depending upon the type of communication service used.

## Visual Display Terminals

Visual display terminals provide visual presentation of information stored within a computer system. These terminals are connected to the computer by data communication channels.

Visual display terminals are used for inquiry to the memory of a computer system. The terminal consists of a keyboard, a signal generator-interpreter, a buffer, and a visual display screen similar to a television screen. (*Figure 45.*)

Figure 44. Stewart-Warner Corporation's "dial/Datafax" transmits and receives facsimile information over voice grade communication channels. The equipment shown includes the compatible DATA-PHONE data set and is for two-way service.

An operator queries the computer system for desired information by pressing the keys. Coded signals are generated and transmitted by means of the data sets over the communication channel to the computer system. The computer system is also equipped with its data set. The computer interprets the signals and searches its memory for the desired information. The information is transmitted, again using the data sets, back over the communication channel to the visual display terminal in the form of coded signals. The signals are interpreted and visually displayed on the screen.

Figure 45. This inquiry display unit is a Teleregister product of the Bunker-Ramo Corporation. The inquiry is made using the keyboard. The inquiry and answer from the computer are displayed on the television-type screen.

# COMMUNICATION SERVICES

## DATA-PHONE Service

DATA-PHONE service provides for the transmission of data using regular dialed-up telephone service. This is accomplished using data sets and the same dial telephone network that is used for local or long distance voice communications. A DATA-PHONE data set has a telephone associated with it and the data set is connected to a business machine terminal. The data set may be connected electrically or acoustically to the telephone network. The data set converts the electrical signals from the compatible business machine into tones suitable for transmission over the telephone network and provides the means for dialing the call.

To place a data call, the user lifts the telephone receiver associated with the DATA-PHONE data set, receives dial tone, and dials the telephone number associated with the DATA-PHONE data set at the receiving business machine terminal.

At the receiving terminal, the call is answered at the DATA-PHONE data set either automatically or manually by an attendant. When answered by an attendant, the sets are in the normal "talk" or "voice" mode. The operators then talk and confirm with each other that the business machine terminals are ready to transmit or receive data.

When all is ready, the operators switch the established telephone connection from the "talk" mode to the "data" mode by pressing the "data" button on the DATA-PHONE data set. This action transfers control of the line to the business machine terminals, enabling the machines to transmit and receive data. *(Figure 46.)*

At the completion of transmission, the operators press the "talk" buttons and hang up the telephones, thereby disconnecting the call.

There are also DATA-PHONE data sets available that automatically establish calls for the transmission of data between business machine terminals without the aid of any operators. This is possible by using a device called an Automatic Calling Unit. When directed by the associated business machine, this device automatically dials the telephone call. These units are capable of dialing telephone calls by using the conventional rotary dial technique or the new TOUCH-TONE dialing system.

DATA-PHONE data sets are also arranged to automatically answer calls. This unattended answer feature permits an unattended location to have its machine turned on automatically by the calling DATA-PHONE data set.

Figure 46. The buttons on the DATA-PHONE data set are used to transfer from the "talk" to the "data" mode of operation.

## Wide Area
## Telephone Service—WATS

WATS is a service used by customers who make many outgoing long distance telephone calls. This service provides the customer with the means for making telephone calls from his premises to telephones anywhere within a specified service area at monthly rates. Two classes of service are offered in WATS: full time and measured time service. Under full time service, the customer is provided an access line which he may use twenty-four hours a day, seven days a week, for outgoing calls to telephones located within the service area for which he subscribes. He pays a flat monthly rate for this service. In measured time service, the access line is also continuously available, but the basic monthly rate covers 15 hours of use of the WATS line per month, for service to telephones within the subscribed-for service area. WATS can be used alternately for voice communications and data transmission using DATA-PHONE service.

The monthly charge for a WATS line is determined by the calling area a particular customer desires. The United States is divided into six calling areas. The calling areas are determined by a percentage of the total number of telephones a customer can reach, and by geographical boundaries. For example, referring to the map shown in *Figure 47,* a customer in Missouri subscribing to Area 1 WATS can call any telephone in the states of Illinois, Kentucky, Tennessee, Arkansas, Oklahoma, Kansas, Nebraska and Iowa. It should be noted that the home state of Missouri is not included in WATS Area 1. The home state is a separate calling area. Should this same customer subscribe to Area 2 WATS, the states in Area 1 would also be included, and so forth across the country. Subscribing to Area 6 WATS entitles a customer to call anywhere in the continental United States except Alaska and the home state. Service within the home state may be subscribed to separately in those states where intrastate service is offered.

**Teleprinter
Exchange Services**

Teleprinter exchange services provide direct dial point-to-point connections using teleprinter equipment such as keyboard printers, paper tape readers and paper tape punches. The service is provided

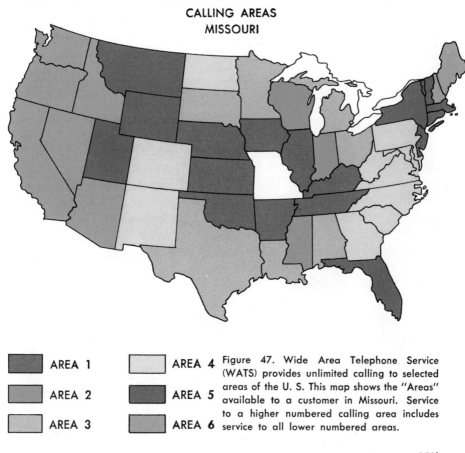

CALLING AREAS
MISSOURI

AREA 1

AREA 2

AREA 3

AREA 4

AREA 5

AREA 6

Figure 47. Wide Area Telephone Service (WATS) provides unlimited calling to selected areas of the U. S. This map shows the "Areas" available to a customer in Missouri. Service to a higher numbered calling area includes service to all lower numbered areas.

135

by the communications common carriers and is known by such names as TELEX and Teletypewriter Exchange Service (TWX).

A call is established in the same manner as a telephone call, by dialing from one teleprinter to another. Once the connection is established, operators at the machines converse by typing back and forth, or messages may be sent automatically using paper tape. A teleprinter conversation could be likened to a telephone conversation, except that the communication medium is written instead of oral. The service is available within the continental United States (except Alaska), Canada and Mexico. *(Figure 48.)*

### Overseas Service

Some common carrier communications companies offer overseas communications for voice, written and data service.

Teleprinter exchange services can be used for transmission of messages to points outside the United States through connecting arrangements with international communications companies.

Figure 48. Automatic teleprinter exchange services permit users to dial their calls directly to distant stations. After the call is established conversation takes place using the keyboard. The messages are printed out at both locations simultaneously. Note that the attendant is using push-button dialing.

## Private Line Voice Service

Private line voice service provides circuits for the exclusive use of a particular subscriber. These services may be used alternately for voice communication and data transmission.

A private line can be set up on a two-point or multi-point basis. On a two-point arrangement there are no signaling problems. Since both points are connected at all times, one point can ring the other by simply pushing a button. However, on a multi-point line, each individual point is assigned a separate code, and selection arrangements can be made on a manual pushbutton basis or on an automatic dial basis. Charges for private line service are based upon mileage and the number of stations on the network.

## Private Line
## Teleprinter Service

Private line teleprinter service provides circuits for the exclusive use of a particular subscriber. Keyboard printers, paper tape punches and paper tape readers are used with these services. One circuit can connect two or more teleprinter machines. In the case of a multi-point circuit, manual or automatic selection between separate teleprinters is available, similar to private line voice service. Charges for this service are also based upon mileage.

## Telpak Service

Telpak[1] is a private line service that provides communications capacities of various sizes suitable for large-volume point-to-point transmission of voice, data, or other forms of communication. Telpak capacities can be arranged so that they constitute a group of voice channels suitable for use for voice or data communications or a group of channels suitable for use with teleprinter equipment. The Telpak capacity can also be used as a single large channel for high-speed data services such as magnetic tape, computer memory and facsimile transmission.

For example, one Telpak "C" channel, which is the equivalent of 60 voice grade channels, can be used for high-speed transmission at a speed of 15,000 characters per second. Telpak "A", "B" and "D" are equivalent to 12, 24, and 240 voice channels, respectively.

Channel capacities similar to that of Telpak are also available with privately owned microwave systems.

---

[1] The Federal Communications Commission in December, 1964, issued a decision holding that rates for certain portions of the interstate Telpak service are unreasonably discriminatory and ordering the filing of revised tariffs. The Commission further ordered that additional cost data be submitted from which the propriety of the rates for other portions of interstate Telpak service can be determined. In August 1965, the United States Court of Appeals for the District of Columbia Circuit stayed the Commission's orders pending a review by the Court.

# COMMUNICATION SWITCHING

Whenever information is to be sent within a pattern of many locations connected to many other locations, some arrangement must be made to enable two stations to communicate with each other. As described in Chapter 5, the connection may be a permanent one in which every station has a private line to every other station. This is, however, a very expensive arrangement and generally not practical for large networks. A more economical and flexible arrangement is to provide for a temporary connection between the two stations wishing to exchange information. The process of temporarily connecting two stations together is called switching.

There are two basic methods of performing the switching function: line switching and message switching. In line switching the lines of the two stations wishing to exchange information are electrically connected together. In message switching the sending and receiving lines are not directly connected. All the lines are, however, connected to the switching center. The message is sent from the sending location into the switching center which may store the message and then later retransmit that message to the proper receiving location.

These two methods of switching are quite different and an understanding of data communications should include some knowledge of the two types.

### Line Switching

The most important difference between the two systems is the way in which the connections are set up. In line switching the calling station first sends to the switching center the address of the station to which the information is to be sent. This is similar to the process of dialing a number when making a regular telephone call. On the basis of the addressing information, the switching center selects the line of the called station and connects the calling and called lines together. Only after the switching function has been completed can the transfer of information take place. During communication the two stations involved are in direct contact.

### Message Switching

In message switching the originating station sends its message directly into the switching center along with the necessary addressing information. The switching center stores the message, examines the addressing information in the heading of the message and then transmits the message to the proper location(s). The sending station does not wait on the line for the message to reach its destination. It simply sends its message to the switching center and then "hangs up." The stored message can be retransmitted at any time. It may be sent out immediately or, if the distant station is busy, the message will be held in storage until that station is available to receive the message.

In a message switching system the originating and receiving stations never communicate directly. Instead, the message is passed along on a store and forward basis.

## Comparison of the Two Systems

**Speed of communication.** In a message switching system the overall delivery time of a message may be longer than in a line switching system depending upon how long the message is held in storage enroute.

**Codes.** In line switching, the code used to give the address information is usually different from the code used to send the message. The dialing signals, for example, which are used to set up the telephone connection are not the same as the language used to exchange information. In fact, once a line-switch connection is set up, the communications channel is insensitive to the language, code, format, or (within limits) the speed of transmission.

In message switching systems, however, this is not usually the case. Because the messages are held in storage and may move through more than one switching center, it is desirable to have the addressing information in the same language as the message. This permits each switching location to examine the heading of the message to determine what should be done with it and where it should be sent. This means that a message switching system is language-sensitive; i.e., the switching center must be able to read the information in the message.

**Servicing the message.** One of the most important advantages of a message switching system is its ability to perform special services for the message. The switching center can, for example, as mentioned above, send the same message to a number of addresses. In a line switching system this could be done by multiple calls or setting up a conference connection and sending to all the parties at once. These methods are cumbersome and time consuming.

In message switching the message is sent to the switching center with the multiple addressing information in the message. This could even be a short code which the switching center can interpret as a group of many addresses. Since the message is stored in the switching center, the center can send the message to each receiving location automatically. If some stations are busy, the center can call them back later.

The message switching center can perform other operations as well. It can insert time of day and other data into messages; it can number messages sequentially, provide speed and code conversion, supervise station polling, give system status reports, provide traffic statistics, etc.

**Efficiency.** Message switching has the advantage that the originating station can send a message into the switching center at any time, regardless of whether the receiving station(s) or intermediate circuits are busy. In line switching, where the complete communications path must be set up before the stations can communicate, the probability that any link in the chain will be busy must be kept very low, or there will be a good chance that the calls cannot be completed. In general, this means that a line switching system will need more circuits and stations than a message switching system to handle a comparable amount of traffic. Since the message switching system can hold messages in storage until the lines or stations are available, the lines and stations can be used more efficiently but may also involve longer delays.

**Type of connection.** The fact that the two stations are in direct contact in a line switching system permits a two-way "chit-chat" type of communication. A message switching system introduces some delay which might not be tolerable in some types of on-line operations.

**Message assurance.** In a line switching system the receiving station can directly acknowledge the receipt of a message. This prevents messages from getting lost in transmission. In a message switching system, however, the sending station is not on the line when the message is delivered to the receiving station. This means that some assurance of delivery should be given to the sending station. Usually this is done by (1) a system of sequentially numbering messages and checking for lost messages by watching all locations for missing numbers in the sequence, (2) a link by link acknowledgment, or (3) by sending a separate message of acknowledgment back to the originator.

140

It can be seen that each type of system has its advantages and disadvantages. Line switching is characteristic, of course, of normal telephone transmission and is usually required for on-line real-time systems. For most other types of data communication systems, message switching is likely to be more economical. In the larger information systems it is becoming apparent that a combination of both line and message switching techniques will have to be employed to provide the necessary data communication services.

# GLOSSARY OF DATA COMMUNICATIONS TERMS

The concept of data communications has given rise to many new technical words and expressions and has caused redefinition of many others already in wide use among computer specialists. This glossary is largely limited to those terms which are associated with data communications but some data processing terms that are important to a better understanding of data communications have also been included.

Whenever possible the definitions in this glossary were taken directly from the proposed American Standards Association's Standard Vocabulary for Information Processing. The remainder of the terms have either been adapted from other glossaries or were specially written for this glossary.

**ASCII**

American *S*tandard *C*ode for *I*nformation *I*nterchange. This is the code established as an American standard by the American Standards Association.

**Alternate Route**

A secondary communications path used to reach a destination if the primary path is unavailable.

**Audio**

Frequencies which can be heard by the human ear (usually between 15 cycles and 20,000 cycles per second).

**Automatic Calling Unit (ACU)**

A dialing device supplied by the communication common carriers which permits a business machine to automatically dial calls over the communication networks.

**Bandwidth**

The difference, expressed in cycles per second, between the highest and lowest frequencies of a band.

**Baseband**

In the process of modulation, the baseband is the frequency band occupied by the aggregate of the transmitted signals when first used to modulate a carrier.

### Batch Processing

A method of processing in which a number of similar input items are accumulated and processed together.

### Baud

A unit of signaling speed. In an equal length code, one baud corresponds to a rate of one signal element per second. Thus, with a duration of the signal element of 20 milliseconds, the modulation rate is 50 bauds (per second).

### Baudot Code

A code for the transmission of data in which five bits represent one character. It is named for Emile Baudot, a pioneer in printing telegraphy. The name is usually applied to the code used in many teleprinter systems and which was first used by Murray, a contemporary of Baudot.

### Bit

A unit of information content. Contraction of "binary digit," a bit is the smallest unit of information in a binary system of notation. It is the choice between two possible states, usually designated one and zero.

### Bit Rate

The speed at which bits are transmitted, usually expressed in bits per second.

### Block Diagram

A diagram of a system, instrument, computer or program in which selected portions are represented by annotated boxes and interconnecting lines.

### Broadcast

The dissemination of information to a number of stations simultaneously.

### Buffer

A storage device used to compensate for a difference in rate of flow of data or time of occurrence of events, when transmitting data from one device to another.

**Busy Hour**

The peak 60-minute period during a business day when the largest volume of communications traffic is handled.

**Carriage Return**

In a character-by-character printing mechanism, the operation that causes the next character to be printed at the left margin.

**Carrier System**

A means of obtaining a number of channels over a single path by modulating each channel upon a different "carrier" frequency and demodulating at the receiving point to restore the signals to their original form.

**Cathode Ray Tube (CRT)**

A television-like picture tube used in visual display terminals.

**Central Office**

The place where communications common carriers terminate customer lines and locate the equipment which interconnects those lines.

**Channel**

A path for electrical transmission between two or more points. Also called a circuit, facility, line, link or path.

**Character**

The actual or coded representation of a digit, letter, or special symbol.

**Circuit**

See channel.

**Code**

A system of symbols and rules for use in representing information.

**Code Conversion**

The conversion of data from one code to another.

**Communications Common Carrier**

A company which dedicates its facilities to a public offering of universal communication services, and which is subject to public utility regulation.

**Computer Utility**

A service which provides computational ability. A "time-shared" computer system. Programs as well as data may be made available to the user. The user also may have his own programs immediately available in the central processor, may have them on call at the computer utility or he may load them by transmitting them to the computer prior to using them. Certain data and programs are shared by all users of the service; other data and programs because of proprietary nature have restricted access. Computer utilities are generally accessed by means of data communications subsystems. Also see Service Bureau.

### Conversation Mode

A procedure for communication between a terminal and the computer in which each entry from the terminal elicits a response from the computer and vice versa.

### Data

Any representations such as characters or analog quantities to which meaning might be assigned.

### Data Collection

The act of bringing data from one or more points to a central point.

### Data Communications

The movement of encoded information by means of electrical transmission systems.

### Data Origination

The earliest stage at which the source material is first put into machine readable form or directly into electrical signals.

### DATA-PHONE

A trade mark of the A.T.&T. Company to identify the data sets manufactured and supplied by the Bell System for use in the transmission of data over the regular telephone network. It is also a service mark of the Bell System which identifies the transmission of data over the regular telephone network (DATA-PHONE Service).

### Data Processing

Any operation or combination of operations on data.

### Data Set

A device which converts between the signals of a business machine and signals that are suitable for transmission over communication lines. It may also perform other related functions.

## Data Transmission

See data communications.

## Demodulation

The process of retrieving an original signal from a modulated carrier wave. This technique is used in data sets to make communication signals compatible with business machine signals.

## Dial-Up

The use of a dial or push-button telephone to initiate a station-to-station telephone call.

## Direct Distance Dialing

A telephone service which enables a user to dial directly telephones outside the user's local area without the aid of an operator.

## Display Unit

A device which provides a visual representation of data.

## Duplex

In communications, pertaining to a simultaneous two-way and independent transmission in both directions (sometimes referred to as "full duplex"). Contrast with half-duplex.

## Error

Any discrepancy between a computed, observed, or measured quantity and the true, specified, or theoretically correct value or condition.

## Error Control

An arrangement that will detect the presence of errors. In some systems, refinements are added that will correct the detected errors, either by operations on the received data or by retransmission from the source.

## Exchange

A defined area, served by a communications common carrier, within which the carrier furnishes service at the exchange rate and under the regulations applicable in that area as prescribed in the carrier's filed tariffs.

## Facility

See channel.

## Facsimile (FAX)

Transmission of pictures, maps, diagrams, etc. The image is

146

scanned at the transmitter, reconstructed at the receiving station and duplicated on some form of paper.

## Foreign Exchange Service

A service which connects a customer's telephone to a remote exchange. This service provides the equivalent of local service from the distant exchange.

## Full Duplex

See duplex.

## Half-Duplex

Pertaining to an alternate, one-way-at-a-time, independent transmission (sometimes referred to as "single"). Contrast with duplex.

## Hard Copy

A printed copy of machine output in readable form for human beings; for example, reports, listings, documents, summaries.

## Holding Time

The length of time a communication channel is in use for each transmission. Includes both message time and operating time.

## Information

The meaning assigned to data by known conventions.

## Information Retrieval

That branch of computer technology concerned with techniques for storing and searching large quantities of information and making selected information available. An information retrieval system may or may not be a real-time system.

## In-Plant System

A data handling system confined to one building or a number of buildings in one locality.

## Input

1. The data to be processed. 2. The state or sequence of states occurring on a specified input channel. 3. The device or collective set of devices used for bringing data into another device. 4. A channel for impressing a state on a device or logic element. 5. The process of transferring data from an external storage to an internal storage.

## Interface

A shared boundary, for example, the boundary between two subsystems or two devices.

**Laser**

A maser which operates at optical frequencies.

**LDX**

*Long Distance Xerography.* A name used by the Xerox Corporation to identify its high speed facsimile system. The system uses Xerox terminal equipment and a wide band data communication channel.

**Line**

See channel.

**Line Switching**

The switching technique of temporarily connecting two lines together so that the stations directly exchange information.

**Link**

See channel.

**Local Channel**

A channel connecting a communications subscriber to a central office.

**Maser**

A device capable of amplifying or generating radiation. Maser amplifiers are used in satellite communication ground stations to amplify the extremely weak signals received from communications satellites.

**MICR**

*Magnetic Ink Character Recognition.* Machine recognition of characters printed with magnetic ink. Contrast with OCR.

**Message**

A communication, prepared for information interchange, in a form suitable for passage through the interchange medium. It includes: (a) all portions of the communication such as machine sensible controls, (b) an indication of the start of the message and the end of the message, and (c) a heading containing routing and other information, one or more texts containing the originator-to-addressee communication(s), and the end of text indicator.

**Message Format**

Rules for the placement of such portions of a message as message heading, address, text, and end of message.

## Message Retrieval

The capability to retrieve a message some time after it has entered an information system.

## Message Numbering

The identification of each message within a communications system by the assignment of a sequential number.

## Message Switching

The switching technique of receiving a message, storing it until the proper outgoing circuit and station are available, and then retransmitting it toward its destination.

## Microwave

All electromagnetic waves in the radio frequency spectrum above 890 megacycles per second.

## Mnemonic Address

A simple address code that has some easily remembered relationship to the name of the destination, e.g., LA for Los Angeles, ATL for Atlanta.

## Modem

Contraction of modulator-demodulator. A device which modulates and demodulates signals transmitted over communication facilities.

## Modulation

The process by which some characteristic of one wave is varied in accordance with another wave. This technique is used in data sets to make business-machine signals compatible with communication facilities.

## Multiple Address Message

A message to be delivered to more than one destination.

## Multiplexing

The division of a transmission facility into two or more channels.

## Multipoint Circuit

A circuit interconnecting several stations.

## Network

1. A series of points interconnected by communications channels.
2. The switched telephone network is the network of telephone lines normally used for dialed telephone calls. 3. A private line

network is a network of communications channels confined to the use of one customer.

## OCR

Optical Character Recognition. The machine recognition of printed or written characters based on inputs from photoelectric transducers. Contrast with MICR.

## Off-Line

Pertaining to equipment or devices not under direct control of the central processing unit. May also be used to describe terminal equipment which is not connected to a transmission line.

## On-Line

Pertaining to peripheral equipment or devices in direct communication with the central processing unit. May also be used to describe terminal equipment which is connected to a transmission line.

## One-Way Channel

A channel which permits transmission in one direction only.

## Operating Time

The time required for dialing the call, waiting for the connection to be established, and coordinating the forthcoming transaction with the personnel or equipment at the receiving end.

## Output

1. Data that has been processed. 2. The state or sequence of states occurring on a specified output channel. 3. The device or collective set of devices used for taking data out of a device. 4. A channel for expressing a state of a device or logic element. 5. The process of transferring data from an internal storage to an external storage device.

## Parallel Transmission

Method of information transfer in which all bits of a character are sent simultaneously. Contrast with serial transmission.

## PICTURE-PHONE

A telephone service that permits the user to see as well as talk with the person at the distant end.

## Page Copy

See hard copy.

**Path**

See channel.

**Perforator**

A keyboard device for punching paper tape.

**Print-Out**

See hard copy.

**Polling**

A centrally controlled method of calling a number of points to permit them to transmit information.

**Priority or Precedence**

Controlled transmission of messages in order of their designated importance, e.g., urgent or routine.

**Private Line or Private Wire**

A channel or circuit furnished a subscriber for his exclusive use.

**Punched Paper Tape**

A strip of paper on which characters are represented by combinations of punched holes.

**Real Time**

1. Pertaining to the actual time during which a physical process takes place. 2. Pertaining to the performance of a computation during a period short in comparison with the actual time that the related physical process takes place in order that results of the computations can be used in guiding the physical process.

**Redundancy**

The portion of the total information contained in a message which can be eliminated without loss of essential information.

**Reperforator**

A device that automatically punches a paper tape from received signals.

**Response Time**

The amount of time elapsed between generation of an inquiry at a data communications terminal and receipt of a response at that same terminal. Response time, thus defined, includes:
Transmission time to the computer,
Processing time at the computer, including access time to obtain any file records needed to answer the inquiry, and
Transmission time back to the terminal.

151

## Selective Calling

The ability of a transmitting station to specify which of several stations on the same line is to receive a message.

## Serial Transmission

A method of information transfer in which the bits composing a character are sent sequentially. Contrast with parallel transmission.

## Service Bureau

An installation where the user can lease processing time on a central processor and peripheral equipment. The user supplies the programs and the center will load both program and data to be processed, process the data and deliver the results to the user. The program and data for processing may be delivered or sent between user and center in any of several forms: cards, punched tape, magnetic tape, etc. Data communications may be used between the user and the center to move the information electrically. The service bureau may also provide such services as keypunching the data and preparing it for processing. Also see computer utility.

## Simplex Channel

See one-way channel.

## Single-Address Message

A message to be delivered to only one destination.

## Station

One of the input or output points on a communications system.

## Status Reports

A term used to describe the automatic reports generated by a message-switching system generally covering service conditions such as circuits and stations out of service and back in service.

## Storage

A general term for any device capable of retaining information.

## Store-and-Forward

Process of message handling used in a message-switching system.

## Stunt-Box

A device to control the non-printing functions of a teleprinter terminal. Control characters can be sent to it over the communications channel.

152

## Tariff

The published rate for a specific unit of equipment, facility or type of service provided by a communication common carrier.

## Telegraphy

A system of communication for the transmission of graphic symbols, usually letters or numerals, by use of a signal code.

## Telegraphy, Printing

A method of telegraph operation in which the received signals are automatically recorded in printed characters.

## Teleprinter

Term used to refer to the equipment used in a printing telegraph system. A teletypewriter.

## Teleprinter Exchange Service

A service provided by communication common carriers to interconnect teleprinters. Similar to regular telephone service, customers dial calls from station to station but communicate using teleprinter equipment rather than telephones.

## Tele-processing

A form of information handling in which a data processing system utilizes communication facilities.

## Teletype

Trademark of the Teletype Corporation. Usually refers to a series of different types of teleprinter equipment such as transmitters, tape punches, reperforators, page printers, utilized for communication systems.

## Teletypewriter

Term used by the Bell System to refer specifically to teleprinter equipment.

## Teletypewriter Exchange Service (TWX)

An automatic teleprinter exchange switching service provided by the Bell System.

## Telex

An automatic teleprinter exchange switching service provided by Western Union.

## Telpak

A service offered by communications common carriers for the leasing of wide band channels between two or more points.

## Terminal

1.  A point at which information can enter or leave a communication network.

2.  An input/output device designed to receive or send source data in an environment associated with the job to be performed and capable of transmitting entries to and obtaining output from the system of which it is a part.

## Text

That part of the message which contains the substantive information to be conveyed. Sometimes called "body" of the message.

## Tie Line

A private line communication channel of the type provided by communications common carriers for linking two or more points together.

## Time-Sharing

A method of operation in which a computer facility is shared by several users for different purposes at (apparently) the same time. Although the computer actually services each user in sequence, the high speed of the computer makes it appear that the users are all handled simultaneously.

## Torn-Tape Switching Center

A location where operators tear off incoming printed and punched paper tape and transfer it manually to the proper outgoing circuit.

## Touch-Tone

A service mark of the American Telephone and Telegraph Company which identifies its pushbutton dialing service.

## TWX

See Teletypewriter Exchange Service.

## Unattended Operation

The automatic features of a station's operation which permit the transmission and reception of messages on an unattended basis.

## Voice Grade Channel

A channel suitable for transmission of speech, digital or analog data, or facsimile, generally with a frequency range of about 300 to 3000 cycles per second.

## Volatile Display

The non-permanent image appearing on the screen of a visual display terminal.

## WATS

See Wide Area Telephone Service.

## Wide Area Telephone Service

A service provided by Telephone Companies which permits a customer by use of an access line to make calls to telephones in a specific zone on a dial basis for a flat monthly charge.

## Wideband Channel

A channel wider in bandwidth than a voice grade channel.

## Word

1. In telegraphy, six characters (five characters plus one space).

2. In computing, an ordered set of characters which is the normal unit in which information may be stored, transmitted, or operated upon within a computer.

# DATA COMMUNICATIONS BIBLIOGRAPHY

## BOOKS

Bennett, W. R. and Davey, J. R., *Data Transmission.* McGraw-Hill Book Company, Inc., New York, 1965.

Buckingham, Walter, *Automation: Its Impact on Business and People.* Mentor Executive Library Books, New York, 1963 (particularly Chapter 3).

Cherry, Colin, *On Human Communication.* John Wiley and Sons, Inc., New York, 1961.

Dunlop, John T., *Automation and Technological Change.* Prentice-Hall, Inc., Englewood Cliffs, N. J., 1962 (particularly Chapters 3 and 4).

Englebardt, Stanley L., *Computers.* Pyramid Publications, Inc., New York (Chapters 12, 13, 14, and 17).

Greenberger, Martin, Editor, *Management and the Computer of the Future.* John Wiley & Sons, Inc., New York, 1962.

Halacy, D. S., Jr., *Computers—The Machines We Think With.* Dell Publishing Co., Inc., New York, 1962 (Chapters 10 and 11).

Head, Robert V., *Real-Time Business Systems.* Holt, Rinehart and Winston, Inc., New York, 1964.

Marteno, R. L., *Project Management and Control,* 3 Volumes, American Management Association, New York, 1964.

McDonough, Adrian M., *Information Economics and Management Systems.* McGraw-Hill Book Company, Inc., New York, 1963.

Quirk, William B., "Data Transmission for Display Purposes," *Electronic Information Display Systems,* James H. Howard (Ed.), Spartan Books, Inc., Washington, D.C., 1963.

## PERIODICALS

Alden, Wm. L., "Cutting Communications Costs with Facsimile." *Data Processing* Vol. 6, No. 9, September, 1964.

Aldridge, C. A., "Growing Significance of Display Systems and Related Techniques." *Data Systems Design* Vol. 1, No. 9, September, 1964.

Alexander, A. A., R. M. Gryb and D. W. Nast, "Capabilities of the Telephone Network for Data Transmission," *The Bell System Technical Journal* Vol. 39, May, 1960.

Atwood, James, Jack Volder, and Gerald Yutzi, "Data Central Message Switching Systems." *Datamation* Vol. 11, No. 2, February, 1965.

"Automated Ordering Ups Retail Sales." *Journal of Data Management* Vol. 2, No. 4, April, 1964.

"Automatic Message Switching and Processing System Utilized by Airline." *Journal of Machine Accounting* Vol. 15, No. 11, November, 1964.

Beauchamp, Dale R., "Data Network Speeds Plant-Dealer-Customers Service." *Journal of Machine Accounting* Vol. 15, No. 6, June, 1964.

Berk, M. A. & Haugh, C. F., "Matching Communications Facilities to Data Processing," *Computers & Automation* Vol. 13, No. 10, October, 1964.

Birmingham, Donald J., "Planning for Data Communications." *Data Processing* Vol. 6, No. 10, October, 1964.

156

## Periodicals (cont'd)

Bonney, Joseph B., "Perceptive Feedback." *Data Processing* Vol. 6, No. 8, August, 1964.

Brett, J. J., "Breaking the Input Bottleneck." *Computers & Data Processing* Vol. 1, No. 6, June, 1964.

Brown, George, "New York Central Breaks Data 'Bottleneck'." *Journal of Data Management* Vol. 2, No. 4, April, 1964.

Caleo, Robert L., "What's Happening in the Office?" *Administrative Management* Vol. 25, No. 1, January, 1964.

Cheek, R. C., "Establishing the Telecomputer Center." *Journal of Data Management* Vol. 2, No. 6, June, 1964.

"Data-Phone Links Stock Ordering." *Journal of Data Management* Vol. 3, No. 2, February, 1965.

Dearden, John, "Can Management Information be Automated?" *Harvard Business Review*, March-April, 1964, pp. 128-35.

Dee, R. G., "Computers, Communications Become Interdependent." *Data Processing* Vol. 6, No. 11, November, 1964.

"Display System Pictorial Report." *Computers & Automation* Vol. 13, No. 5, May, 1964.

Duke, William M., "Information System Automation—Good or Bad?" *Computers & Data Processing* Vol. 1, No. 1, January, 1964.

"Electronic Buying Via Telematic System." *Journal of Machine Accounting*, Vol. 15, No. 10, October, 1964.

*Fortune.* See 1964 issues, especially the August and November issues.

"Function and Application of Data-Phone Service." *Journal of Machine Accounting*, Vol. 15, No. 2, February, 1964.

Galley, Thomas A., "The Key to On-Line Systems." *Journal of Data Management*, Vol. 2, No. 7, July, 1964.

Garchow, A. R., "Automated Transmission of Credit Data." *Credit World*, November, 1964.

Garrity, John T., "The Management Information Dread: The End or a New Beginning?" *Financial Executive*, Vol. 32, No. 9, September, 1964.

Gentle, Edgar C., Jr., "Function and Application of Data-Phone Service," *Public Utilities Fortnightly*, Vol. 72, No. 10, November 7, 1963.

Gentle, Edgar C., Jr., "Keeping Management Up to the Minute," *Computers and Data Processing*, Vol. 1, No. 5, May, 1964.

Gentle, Edgar C., Jr., "Keying the Executive to Real Time Concepts," *Bell Telephone Magazine*, Summer 1964, Vol. XLIII, No. 2.

Greenberger, Martin, "Banking and the Information Utility." *Computers & Automation*, Vol. 14, No. 4, April, 1965.

Head, Robert V., "Programming the Real-Time System." *Journal of Data Management*, Vol. 2, No. 2, February, 1964.

Head, Robert V., "Testing Real-Time Systems—Part 1." *Datamation*, Vol. 10, No. 7, July, 1964.

Head, Robert V., "Testing of Real-Time Systems—Part 2: Levels of Testing." *Datamation*, Vol. 10, No. 8, August, 1964.

Hodskins, James A., "Paper Tape Versus Punched Cards." *Journal of Data Management*, Vol. 2, No. 7, July, 1964.

Isbell, R. D., "Data System Speeds SIU Library Procedure." *Journal of Data Management*, Vol. 2, No. 12, December, 1964.

Jacobs, Robert C., "Central Data System Tightens Management Control." *Journal of Machine Accounting* Vol. 15, No. 4, April, 1964.

James, Glennon J., "Planning a Communication-Based Management Informa-System." *Computers & Automation* Vol. 13, No. 10, October, 1964.

Johnson, Robert W., "Digital Data Display Systems: An Assessment." *Computers & Automation* Vol. 13, No. 5, May, 1964.

Kenney, William J., "The Role of Data Transmission in a Customer Services Program." *Banking*, Vol. 57, No. 1, July, 1964.

Konkel, Paul E., "Management Information Systems Can be Computerized." *Computers & Data Processing* Vol. 1, No. 6, June, 1964.

Kuehn, Rudolph L., "Storage, Retrieval and Conversion of Data." *Data Systems Design* Vol. 1, No. 9, September, 1964.

Laurent, Don and Jack Floyd, "Effective Hospital Management with a Small Computer." *Journal of Machine Accounting* Vol. 15, No. 10, October, 1964.

MacDonald, Neil, "Data Communications Round-Up." *Computers & Automation* Vol. 13, No. 10, October, 1964.

Mapletoft, J. T., "Real-Time Communication System and Management Information." *Systems and Procedures Journal,* Vol. 16, No. 2, March-April, 1965.

Martino, Rocco L., "Creating the Integrated Management System." *Computers & Data Processing,* Vol. 1, No. 4, April, 1964.

McMains, Harvey J. and John W. Emling, "The Changing World of Communications." *Data Management* Vol. 6, No. 9, June, 1964.

"Medlars Goes 'On-Line'." *Journal of Data Management* Vol. 2, No. Pg 51, September, 1964.

Mitchell, H. F., "The Future of the Switching Computer." *Datamation* Vol. 11, No. 2, February, 1965.

Morris, James, "Breaking Communications Bottlenecks." *Systems—The Magazine of Management Methods* May/June, 1963.

Muschamp, George M., "The Emerging Philosophy of Systems Management." *Journal of Data Management* Vol. 2, No. 10, October, 1964.

Myers, Wilbur C., "Storing Visual Information." *Data Systems Design* Vol. 1, No. 9, September, 1964.

Nolan, Michael F., "Source Data Collections in Automated Business Systems." *Journal of Data Management* Vol. 2, No. 2, February, 1964.

"On-Line Computer Speeds Banking Services." *Journal of Data Management* Vol. 2, No. 7, July, 1964.

Oscar, Irving S., "Development in Data Display Equipment." *Data Systems Design* Vol. 1, No. 9, September, 1964.

"Pan Am Installing World-Wide Reservation System." *Journal of Data Management* Vol. 3, No. 2, February, 1965.

Paul, G. Stewart, "Western Union's New Service Meets Expanding Data Communication Needs." *Data Processing* Vol. 8, No. 1, January, 1965.

"Plant of 1970 is Here in '64." *Factory,* February, 1964, pp. 62-65.

Ream, Norman J., "On-Line Management Information, Part 1." *Datamation* Vol. 10, No. 3, March, 1964.

Ream, Norman J., "On-Line Management Information System, Part 2." *Datamation* Vol. 10, No. 4, April, 1964.

Repaci, C. M., "Considering Data Communications." *Computers & Data Processing,* Vol. 1, No. 3, March, 1964.

Sprague, Richard E., "On-Line Real-Time Systems—1964." *Management Services,* May-June, 1964, pp. 40-49.

"Time Sharing Systems"—see Sept. 1965 Issue of Data Processing, Vol. 7, No. 9. This issue contains several articles on this subject.

Townsend, R. L. and R. N. Watts, "Effectiveness of Error Control in Data Communications Over the Switched Telephone Network," *The Bell System Technical Journal,* November, 1964, Vol. 43, No. 6.

*Periodicals* (cont'd)

Van Gelder, Hans, "On-Line Stock Quotation." *Datamation* Vol. 10, No. 3, March, 1964.

"Verbal Telephone Reply from Computer Now Possible with New IBM Audio Response Unit." *Journal of Machine Accounting* Vol. 15, No. 4, April, 1964.

Wallace, Robert E., "A Look at Data Communications." *Journal of Data Management* Vol. 2, No. 9, September, 1964.

Weisberg, David E., "A Command Control Information System for the Field Army." *Computers & Automation* Vol. 13, No. 11, November, 1964.

Weisberg, David E., "Computer-Controlled Graphical Display: Its Applications and Market." *Computers & Automation* Vol. 13, No. 5, May, 1964.

Williams, Walter F., "The Growing Data Volume—Can It Be Mastered?" *Business Automation* Vol. 10, No. 5, November, 1963.

Williams, William F., "Storage and Retrieval—A System For Every Need." *Business Automation* Vol. 11, No. 3, March, 1964.

## MISCELLANEOUS

*Advances in EDP and Information Systems.* AMA Management Report No. 62, 1961, American Management Ass'n., Inc., 1515 Broadway, Times Square, N. Y. 36.

*Auerbach Data Communications Reports*—Auerbach Info, Inc., 55 North 17th St., Philadelphia, Pa. 19103 Attn: Mr. R. G. Scott. This report provides information on various types of data commuunications systems and terminal equipment.

*"Data Transmission and Data Processing Dictionary"*—James F. Holmes—John F. Rider, Inc., Publisher, New York. A compilation of terminology in the fields of data processing, telephony, telegraphy, facsimile, and data transmission.

*Office Automation*—Equipment Edition OA Business Publications, Inc. 228 Park Avenue, West, Elmhurst, Illinois. This is a looseleaf binder describing automated data processing equipment. Part II F covers data transmission equipment.

Southmayd, L. H., "Communications for the New Information Systems." *Proceedings of the UNIVAC Users Association*, Fall Conference, September 14, 15, 16, 1964, New York. N. Y.

Strassburg, Bernard—"The Communications Carrier and Management Information Systems", an address by the Chief, Common Carrier Bureau of the Federal Communications Commission before the Institute on Management Information and Data Transfer Systems, October 21, 1965. Sponsored by American University.

*The Information Revolution, The New York Times*, May 23, 1965, Section 11.

# DATA COMMUNICATIONS IN BUSINESS, AN INTRODUCTION

## INDEX

Accounting applications, 24-25, 36-37
Accuracy of information, 68-71
Alternative systems, 74-76
ASCII code, 124

Belated information, 39
BMEWS (Ballistic Missile Early Warning System), 12
Buffer characters, 61
Business information systems, 30-32
  definition, 3
Busy-hour traffic, 64

CADIN (Canadian Integration North), 11
Call Directing Code (CDC), 56
Cash position control, 22, 36
Codes, 66-67
  ASCII, 124
  used for switching, 139
Computers
  and data communications, 81
  remote-inquiry retrieval, 9-10
  transmission control terminals, 129
  voice communication, 85
Control techniques, 22
Conversion, 68
Cost analysis, 73
Critical Path Method, 20, 96-97

Data, compared to information, 2
Data communications
  definition, 1
  function, 4, 6
  relation to data processing, 4
Data-phone service, 133

Data processing
  examples, 3
  relation to data communications, 4
  remote, 37
  shared facilities, 14
Data sets, 118
Distribution of information, 51

Engineering applications, 29
Error detection and correction (EDC), 70
Error rates, 69
Evaluation of alternative systems, 74-76
Expensive information, 45

Facsimile
  high-speed, 92
  terminals, 131
  transmission, 65
Form-out, 61
Full duplex circuit, 54, 65

Handwriting transmission terminals, 129
Horizontal tabulation, 61

Inaccessible information, 44-45
Inaccurate information, 46
Information
  accuracy of, 68-71
  belated, 39
  compared to data, 2
  distribution patterns, 51-59
  expensive, 45
  inaccessible, 44-45
  inaccurate, 46
  language of, 66-68

Information (*continued*)
  mutilated, 47
  outdated, 42-44
  retrieval, 9-10
  urgency of, 65-66
  volume calculation, 58-66
Information explosion, 8-10
Insurance companies, 45
Inventory control, 35
Invoice processing, 25

Keyboard-only devices, 119
Keyboard printers, 120
Knowlegde, accumulation rate, 8-9

Language of information, 66-68
Laser, 93
Law enforcement, 13
Line switching, 138
Loaded costs, 73

Magnetic tape transmission terminals, 126
Marketing applications, 16-17, 28-29
Merged firms, 14
Message switching, 35, 138
  Westinghouse system, 33-34
Meter reading, remote, 92
MICR (Magnetic Ink Character Recognition), 91
Microfilm transmission, 92
Millimeter wave guide, 93
Mutilated information, 47

NASA (National Aeronautics and Space Administration), 13
Nuclear Test Ban Treaty, 45

On-line real-time systems, 81
Optical scanning, 92
Order processing, 35
Ordering system, automated, 17
Organizational planning, 18-20
Outdated information, 42-44
Overseas service, 136

Payroll processing, 24-25, 40
Peak volume, 63
Personnel records, 25-26
Picturephone service, 91
Pollution control, 44
Private line voice service, 137
Problem identification, 50
Production control, 26-27
Punched card transmission terminals, 126
Punched paper tape transmission, 122

Real-time, 81

SACCS (Strategic Air Command Control Systems), 11-12
SAGE (Semi-Automatic Ground Environment), 11
Sales procedures, 28, 44
Satellite communications, 94
Sears, Roebuck and Company, 6
Semi-real time, 83
SPADATS (Space Detection and Tracking System), 12
Switched networks, 12
Switching systems, 138-41

Tele-Computer Center, 32, 35
Telephone, as data input device, 88
Teleprinters
  exchange services, 135
  keyboard printers, 120
  private line service, 137
Telpak service, 137
Terminal equipment, 87
  accuracy, 70
Time sharing, 29, 90, 114, 154
Transmission speeds, 92
Transmission time, 63

U.S. government, data communication systems, 10-13
Urgency of information, 65-66

Vertical tabulation, 61
Visual display terminals, 131
Voice communications, 85
Volume of information, 58-66

WATS (Wide Area Telephone
　　Service), 134
Weather Bureau, U.S., 13
Westinghouse Information System,
　　32-34
Wide-band transmission, 94